Nelson Advanced Modular Science

Organic Pathways:
Synthesis and Analysis

BRIAN CHAPMAN

Thomas Nelson and Sons Ltd
Nelson House Mayfield Road
Walton-on-Thames Surrey
KT12 5PL UK

First published by Thomas Nelson and Sons Ltd 1998

I(T)P® Thomas Nelson is an International Thomson Publishing Company
I(T)P® is used under licence

ISBN 0-17-448259-0
NPN 9 8 7 6 5 4 3 2 1

Typesetting and illustration: Hardlines, Charlbury, Oxfordshire
Printed in Italy by Eurografica S.p.A, Vicenza
Picture Research by Image Select International.

Publishing team:
Acquisitions: Sonia Clark
Editorial management: Simon Bell
Freelance editorial: Geoff Amor
Marketing: Jane Lewis
Production: Suzanne Howarth

Acknowledgements
The authors and publishers are grateful to the following for permission to reproduce copyright images:

Chris Fairclough: 2.1 (top left); 2.20; 2.22; 2.25; 2.31
Environmental Images: 2.32 (Paul Glendell)
Holt Studios International: 2.7, 2.8, 2.10 (top and bottom) (Nigel Cattlin)
Peter Gould: 2.16, 3.6, 3.7, 3.8a and b, 3.9, 3.10, 3.11, 5.9
Philip Harris Ltd: 2.24
Planet Earth Pictures: 2.9 (John Downer)
Pretty Polly Ltd: 2.27
Royal Society of Chemistry: 1.10, 5.1
Science Photo Library: 1.9; 2.1 right, (Geoff Tomkinson); 2.1 bottom left, (Pascal Nieto, Jerrican); 2.4 (Garry Watson); 2.23 (Dr Jeremy Burgess); 2.29 (Peter Menzel); 2.34 (Carlos Goldin)
Still Pictures: 2.33 (Juntanwonsup-Unep)

Contents

Introduction

This textbook is one of a series of four produced in response to a demand from students and their teachers for resource material in support of the chemistry courses which lead to examinations set by Edexcel (London Examinations) [formerly the University of London Examination and Assessment Council (ULEAC)] in the new modular format. There has been a widespread development of modular courses at Advanced level, and ULEAC took this step in September 1994. There is also an ever-present pressure on syllabus writers to introduce new material into syllabuses to ensure that they reflect adequately the role of chemistry in society today, yet the principal core concepts laid down by common agreement and the Qualifications and Curriculum Authority must retain their rightful place. Writers of the new syllabus and these texts have endeavoured to balance these conflicting demands.

There is a bewildering variety of chemistry texts discussing aspects of the subject at an appropriate level for the A-level student, and it is not the intention of this series to divert the attention of students from these. Indeed it is hoped that students will be excited by their study of chemistry and will want to pursue specialist avenues of interest, as countless others have done in years past. However, it is recognised that at certain times students seek a text which will encapsulate in a relatively small volume the outline of necessary study for each of the Edexcel (London Examinations) modules in chemistry.

These volumes are written by the examiners, all experienced teachers, specifically to prepare students for these examinations, and all the necessary basic material of the syllabus is covered. They further prompt and give pointers for further study for the interested student.

We hope that students will find these texts helpful and supportive of their studies at A-level and their preparation for examinations, and also stimulating to further reading in a wider context.

Geoff Barraclough
Chemistry Series Editor

The author
Brian Chapman was formerly Head of Science at Hardenhuish School, Chippenham. He has been a Chief and Principal Examiner for Edexcel (London Examinations) and other Boards for many years.

The chemistry of organic compounds

You have already met some organic chemistry in *Principles of Physical and Organic Chemistry*. It is very important to make sure that your foundation knowledge is sound before you try to build on it.

Many reactions will be accompanied by diagrams showing mechanisms. Remember that a curved arrow represents the movement of a pair of electrons, which may be shared in a bond or unshared (a lone pair). The arrow should start at the lone pair or at the middle of the bond. If a bond is being formed, the point of the arrow should finish between the bonded atoms; if the bond is being broken and the electrons form a new lone pair, the point of the arrow should finish at the atom or ion with which the lone pair is associated.

For example, in a nucleophilic displacement:

$$HO^-: \quad C-X \rightarrow HO-C + :X^-$$

Alkenes

Sulphuric acid

In *Principles of Physical and Organic Chemistry* you met the addition reactions of alkenes, e.g. ethene (C_2H_4), with halogens (X_2) and hydrogen halides (HX):

$$C_2H_4 + X_2 \rightarrow C_2H_4X_2$$

$$C_2H_4 + HX \rightarrow C_2H_5X$$

The addition of concentrated sulphuric acid to alkenes is similar to the addition of hydrogen halides:

$$\underset{H}{\overset{H}{\diagdown}}C=C\underset{H}{\overset{H}{\diagup}} + H_2SO_4 \rightarrow H-\underset{H}{\overset{H}{C}}-\underset{H}{\overset{H}{C}}-OSO_2OH$$

The resulting alkyhydrogensulphates are much more easily hydrolysed than halides, and they form useful intermediates in the preparation of alcohols:

$$ROSO_2OH + H_2O \rightarrow ROH + H_2SO_4$$

THE CHEMISTRY OF ORGANIC COMPOUNDS

The reaction is used commercially to produce alcohols from alkenes (from petroleum cracking), but, in the case of ethanol, the hydration of ethene uses steam and phosphoric acid (a catalyst) supported on silica at 300 °C and 60 atm. Phosphoric acid is more expensive than sulphuric acid but does not cause oxidation of organic compounds with the formation of impurities and sulphur dioxide.

Addition at unsymmetrical double bonds

A complication arises on the addition of HX (X = Cl, Br, I or HSO_4) to unsymmetrical alkenes, i.e. those in which the molecule differs on either side of the C=C double bond. It was first observed by Markownikov that, in such additions, the H atom of HX joined the carbon atom of the alkene that bore the greater number of hydrogen atoms. This generalisation is known as **Markownikov's rule**. Thus the addition of hydrogen chloride to propene gives predominantly 2-chloropropane:

$$H_3C—CHCl—CH_3 \text{ (major product)}$$

$$H_3C—CH=CH_2$$

$$H_3C—CH_2—CH_2Cl \text{ (minor product)}$$

One method of manufacturing propan-2-ol and propanone from propene depends on this preference:

$$H_3C—CH=CH_2 \xrightarrow{H_2SO_4} H_3C—\underset{OSO_3H}{\underset{|}{CH}}—CH_3 \xrightarrow{H_2O} H_3C—\underset{OH}{\underset{|}{CH}}—CH_3 \xrightarrow{[O]} H_3C.CO.CH_3$$

propene   propan–2–ol   propanone

The reason for Markownikov's rule becomes clear if we look at the mechanism. Consider a simple alkene with a terminal double bond. Initially a carbocation is formed by electrophilic attack on the species by HX. Two carbocations are possible:

OR

Markownikov's rule
When a hydrogen halide is added to a C=C double bond, the hydrogen atom is attached to the carbon atom that already carries more hydrogen.

2

A is a secondary carbocation which is more stable than the primary carbocation **B**. The lower energy of **A** compared with **B** suggests that its formation will require lower activation energy, and thus the formation of **A** will be much faster. The final monochloroalkanes are likely to have similar enthalpies of formation because they have the same bonds present in a different arrangement, but the 2-chloroalkane forms much more quickly and therefore predominates. The reaction is described as kinetically controlled rather than thermodynamically controlled, as would be the case if the ratio of the products depended on their enthalpies of formation.

For everyday problems it is useful to remember and apply Markownikov's rule. However, it is important to understand that it results from the electrophilic addition mechanism with its carbocation intermediates.

Action of manganate(VII)

Oxidation occurs:

ethene   ethane – 1,2 – diol

The manganate(VII) is reduced to green manganate(VI):

$$MnO_4^- + e^- \rightarrow MnO_4^{2-}$$

purple   green

Acidified manganate(VII), especially when hot, is a much more powerful oxidising agent. It is reduced by a large range of organic materials and would be unsuitable as a test. It is also unsuitable for the production of 1,2-diols, as it would oxidise them further: in this case, first to ethanedioic acid and then to carbon dioxide. Ethane-1,2-diol is an important commercial product: it is used as the basis of most antifreezes in car radiators, and it is one of the two starting materials for the manufacture of terylene. The manufacturing process makes ethane-1,2-diol by a two-stage oxidation and hydration of ethene via epoxyethane:

epoxyethane   ethane – 1,2 – diol

QUESTION

Predict the result of the addition of hydrogen iodide to 2-methylbut(2)ene.

Baeyer's test
Alkaline potassium manganate(VII) may be used as a simple laboratory test for double bonds. Alkenes turn the reagent green, but this reaction is given by many reducing agents.

Table 1.1 *Boiling points of primary aliphatic alcohols*

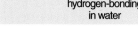

Formula	Name	B.p./°C
CH_3OH	methanol	65
C_2H_5OH	ethanol	78
C_3H_7OH	propanol	97
C_4H_9OH	butanol	117

Alcohols

Introduction

The alcohols are generally pleasant-smelling liquids. The lower members are soluble in water. They owe their relatively high boiling points (Table 1.1) and their solubility in water to the polarity of the O—H group and their ability to form intermolecular **hydrogen bonds** both with alcohol and with water molecules (Figure 1.1).

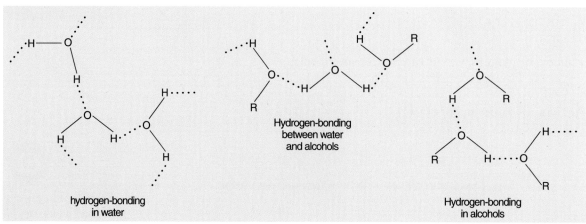

Figure 1.1 Hydrogen-bonding in water and alcohols

Halogenation

In addition to the use of phosphorus pentachloride, the alcohols can also have the —O—H group replaced by the action of halogen acids:

$$ROH + HX \rightleftharpoons RX + H_2O$$

In situ

In situ means "where it is", "in place" or "where it happens to be"

The reaction is much less favourable for HCl than for HBr or HI. In practice, the reaction is seldom done with the halogen acids; one objection is that they already contain water, which shifts the equilibrium to the left. Hydrogen bromide can be generated in situ by using potassium bromide and concentrated sulphuric acid, which are mixed with the alcohol. Hydrogen bromide is always partially oxidised by the sulphuric acid and, apart from the expensive waste of the bromide, this has the effect of contaminating the product with bromine.

Hydrogen iodide is immediately oxidised by concentrated sulphuric acid, and the method is not possible for the preparation of iodides. Instead, a mixture of red phosphorus and iodine acts like phosphorus triiodide:

$$3ROH + PI_3 \rightarrow 3RI + H_3PO_3$$

Concentrated hydrochloric acid can be used but only in the presence of a catalyst, e.g. anhydrous zinc chloride. A better substitute for the relatively expensive phosphorus pentachloride is thionyl chloride, $SOCl_2$:

$$ROH + SOCl_2 \rightarrow RCl + HCl + SO_2$$

However, this has limited use since the halides are almost invariably made as intermediates, and iodides and bromides are far more suitable for this purpose than chlorides.

Dehydration

Alcohols may be dehydrated in many ways. The two most common methods are heating with concentrated sulphuric acid and vapour-phase dehydration by passing the vapour (in the absence of air) over a heated catalyst such as aluminium oxide.

When concentrated sulphuric acid is used in excess, intramolecular elimination of water occurs with the formation of an alkene:

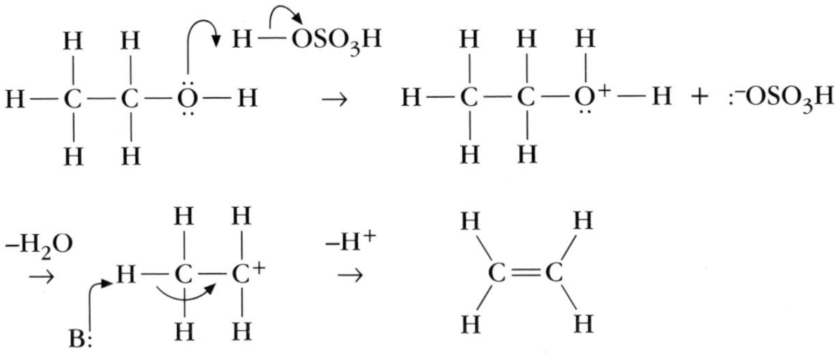

where B: is any proton acceptor, e.g. HSO_4^-

The initially formed oxonium ion can suffer nucleophilic attack by ethanol to give ethoxyethane:

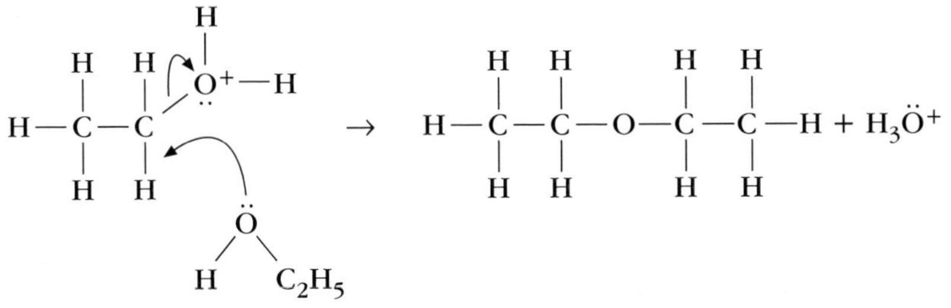

This displacement of water from the intermediate ion occurs more easily (at about 140°C) than intramolecular elimination to give ethene (at about 170°C) if excess ethanol is present. In the presence of excess sulphuric acid, the nucleophile property of the —O: (in the ethanol) would be destroyed by protonation and the positive ions would repel one another.

This elimination reaction must be used in the synthesis of alkenes with some care: the intermediate carbocations sometimes rearrange to more stable forms before loss of the proton. Also, if the alcohol is other than primary, at least two possible alkenes can be formed:

$$H_3C—CH_2—CH_2—CH(OH)—CH_3 \rightarrow H_3C—CH_2—CH{=}CH—CH_3$$
$$\text{or} \qquad\qquad\qquad\qquad \rightarrow H_3C—CH_2—CH_2—CH{=}CH_2$$

These problems are not limited to elimination of water but are true of many elimination reactions that proceed through a carbocation.

Aldehydes and ketones

Introduction

Many organic compounds contain the carbonyl group (>C==O) as *part* of their functional group (e.g. those in Figure 1.2). However, when chemists use the term **carbonyl compound** without qualification, they usually mean aldehydes or ketones (Figure 1.3).

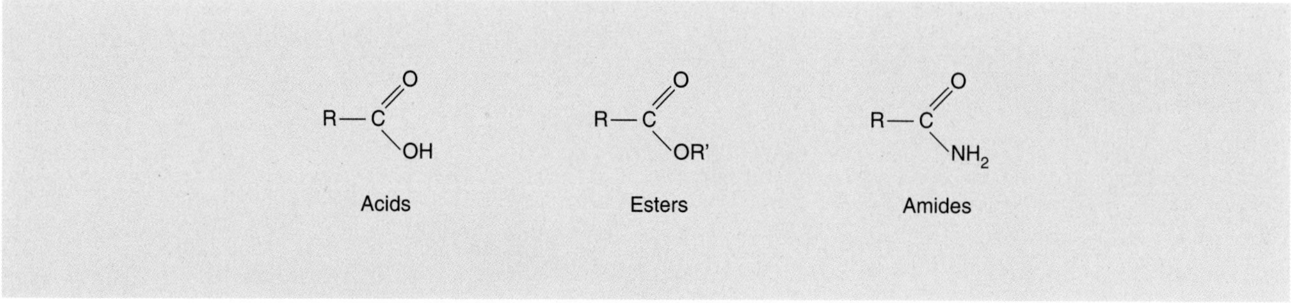

Figure 1.2 Acids, esters and amides contain the carbonyl group in their structures

Figure 1.3 Aldehydes and ketones are carbonyl compounds

With the exception of methanal (HCHO), which is a gas at room temperature, the lower members are volatile liquids (Table 1.2) that are soluble in water. The ketones usually smell more pleasant than the aldehydes. The polarity of the carbonyl group makes the compounds less volatile than alkanes of the same mass, but they are more volatile than the alcohols, which are hydrogen-bonded. The solubility of carbonyl compounds in water is the result both of hydrogen-bonding and addition of the water at the carbonyl group (Figure 1.4).

Table 1.2 *Boiling points of aliphatic aldehydes*

Formula	Name	B.p./°C
HCHO	methanal	−21
CH₃CHO	ethanal	21
C₂H₅CHO	propanal	49
C₃H₇CHO	butanal	75

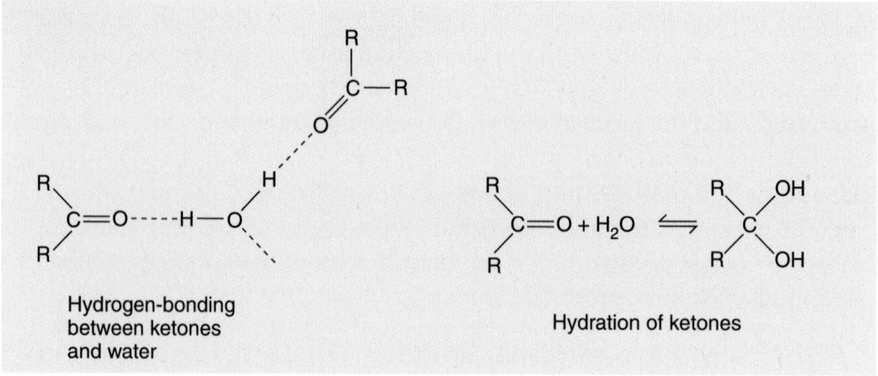

Hydrogen-bonding between ketones and water

Hydration of ketones

Figure 1.4 Hydrogen-bonding and hydration in ketones

With rare exceptions the hydrates are too unstable to be isolated.

Oxidation and reduction

You have already met the oxidation of aldehydes, both as intermediates in the oxidation of primary alcohols and in their capacity to reduce Fehling's or Benedict's solution and ammoniacal silver nitrate. You are reminded that the last two reactions are important for distinguishing between aldehydes (+ve test) and ketones (–ve test).

Normally, ketones are not easy to oxidise, but methyl ketones (-2-ones) can be oxidised by a halogen in alkaline conditions with loss of the methyl carbon atom:

$$R.CO.CH_3 \quad \rightarrow \quad RCO_2H \qquad etc.$$

Whilst this "haloform reaction" has been used to degrade methyl ketones to acids, it has found more use as a test of structure. The test is performed by warming the suspected methyl ketone with iodine and sodium hydroxide (or sodium chlorate(I) and an iodide) and, when positive, gives a yellow precipitate of triiodomethane, CHI_3 (iodoform). Care must be exercised in its interpretation, since it gives a positive test not only with compounds having the structure $CH_3CO—$ but also with compounds with the structure $CH_3CH(OH)—$, which becomes $CH_3CO—$ in the oxidising conditions employed.

The structures in Figures 1.5 and 1.6 represent methyl ketones or methyl secondary alcohols except where R = H, when they are the special cases of ethanal and ethanol, respectively. It is thus very important not to use ethanol as a solvent for this reaction.

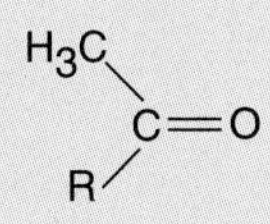

Iodoform test
A methyl ketone, methyl secondary alcohol, ethanal or ethanol on treatment with iodine and aqueous alkali gives a yellow precipitate of iodoform.

H₃C\
\ \
C=O   where R = H, alkyl or aryl\
R/

Figure 1.5 Structure of a methyl ketone

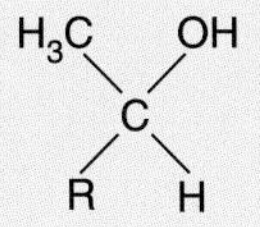

H₃C   OH\
\ /\
C\
/ \\
R   H   where R = H, alkyl or aryl

Figure 1.6 Structure of a methyl secondary alcohol

The course of the reaction may be represented by a variety of equations, but the easiest is shown below for butan-2-ol. If necessary, as here, oxidation first occurs to give a carbonyl compound:

$$CH_3CH(OH)C_2H_5 \quad + \quad I_2 \quad \rightarrow \quad CH_3COC_2H_5 \quad + \quad 2HI$$

Substitution then occurs in the methyl group:

$$CH_3COC_2H_5 \quad + \quad 3I_2 \quad \rightarrow \quad CI_3COC_2H_5 \quad + \quad 3HI$$
1,1,1-triiodobutan-2-one

The electronegativity of the three halogen atoms exerts a strong electron-withdrawing effect on the adjacent C—C bond. The carbonyl group is already withdrawing electrons in the other direction. This lowers the electron density in the C—C bond joining the CI$_3$ to the carbonyl group (Figure 1.7), and nucleophilic attack on the latter is easily followed by fission of this bond:

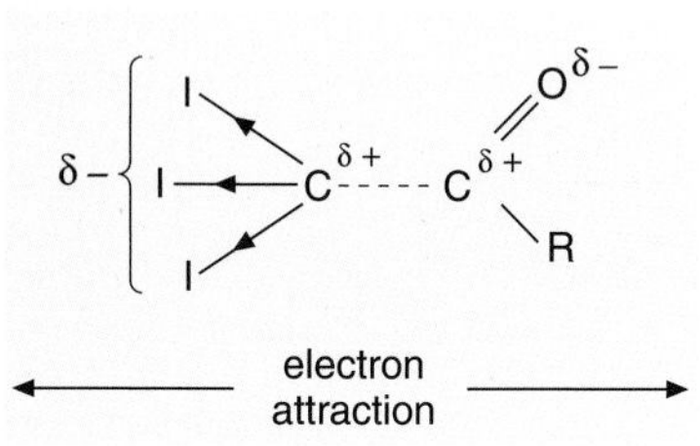

$$I_3C-C-R \rightarrow I_3C-C-R \rightarrow CHI_3 + RCOOH$$

Figure 1.7 Lowering of electron density by triiodomethyl group in bond to be hydrolysed

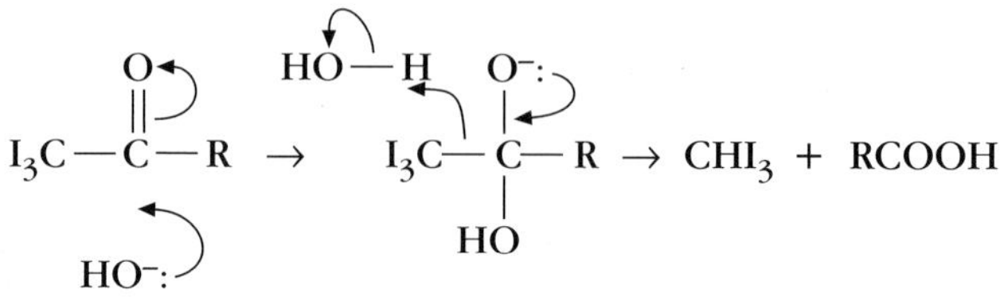

Reductions by lithium aluminium hydride in ether

Lithium aluminium hydride, LiAlH$_4$ (correctly but rarely named lithium tetrahydridoaluminate(III)), in dry ethoxyethane (ether) is capable of reducing all compounds containing the C=O (carbonyl) group. The reagent is expensive and, because it rapidly decomposes in damp conditions, is not easy to store. It is not suitable for industrial reductions except for small-scale use in the drugs industry. The following are examples of reductions of various carbonyl compounds by lithium aluminium hydride:

RCHO → RCH$_2$OH
aldehyde   1° alcohol

RCOR´ → RCH(OH)R´
ketone   2° alcohol

RCOOR´ → RCH$_2$OH + R´OH
ester

RCOOH → RCH$_2$OH
acid

In each reaction, a complex is formed with the aluminium that is stabilised by the dry ether (cf. Grignard reagents, page 17). The mechanisms are rather long and complicated because they involve the successive steps in the substitution of the AlH$_4^-$ ion to give the complex. Reduction may be considered to begin by the nucleophilic addition of the hydride, H$^-$, ion from the AlH$_4^-$ ion at the carbon atom of the carbonyl group:

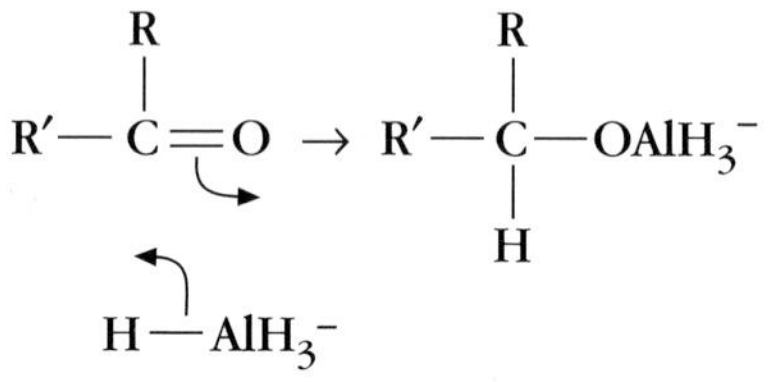

$$R'-C=O \rightarrow R'-C-OAlH_3^-$$

The complex is then decomposed by water to release the alcohol product.

Reduction of carbonyl compounds can be brought about by less expensive reagents than lithium aluminium hydride, such as catalytic hydrogenation or the slightly less powerful sodium borohydride, $NaBH_4$. Sodium borohydride, or sodium tetrahydridoborate(III) as it is seldom called, has the advantage of stability in cold water. Thus not only can it be used in this medium but there is no need for the rigorously anhydrous conditions demanded by its aluminium analogue. The disadvantage is that it will only reduce aldehydes and ketones and not carboxylic acid derivatives.

The initial addition of H^- by $LiAlH_4$ is nucleophilic and suited to reaction with the positively charged carbon of the carbonyl group. Alkenes (see page 1) are susceptible to electrophilic attack and are not affected by $LiAlH_4$. Thus a compound such as 4-oxopentene would probably suffer total reduction by catalytic hydrogenation, but would retain the C==C double bond if reduced by $LiAlH_4$:

$$H_2C{=}CHCH_2COCH_3 \xrightarrow{H_2/Pt} H_3CCH_2CH_2CH(OH)CH_3$$
4-oxopentene

$$H_2C{=}CHCH_2COCH_3 \xrightarrow{LiAlH_4/ether} H_2C{=}CHCH_2CH(OH)CH_3$$

Other nucleophilic reactions at the carbonyl group

Both aldehydes and ketones undergo a wide range of addition and addition–elimination (condensation) reactions. Two will be discussed here: one is of synthetic and one of analytical importance.

Nucleophilic addition of cyanide

Hydrogen cyanide is covalent and a weak acid. To provide the cyanide ion, CN^-, an aqueous solution of sodium or potassium cyanide is used:

an aldehyde cyanohydrin

Aqueous hydrogen cyanide alone is not a suitable reagent since it is a weak acid, and its conjugate base, the cyanide ion, is strong and will remove a proton from water:

$$:CN^- + H_2O \rightleftharpoons HCN + :OH^-$$

Using hydrogen cyanide in the mixture will drive the equilibrium to the left.

The resulting cyanhydrins are of synthetic value, as acid hydrolysis gives α-hydroxyacids:

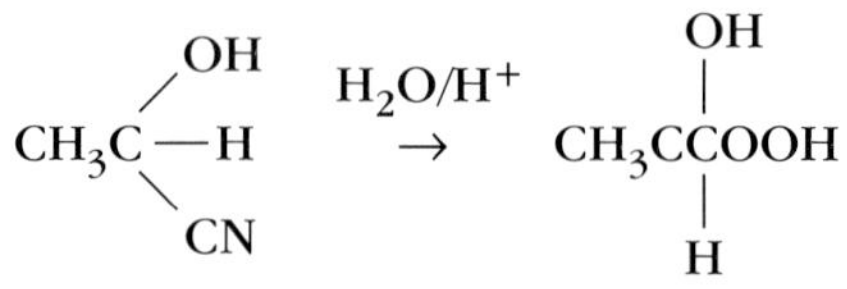

$$CH_3\overset{\displaystyle OH}{\underset{\displaystyle CN}{C}}-H \quad \xrightarrow{\displaystyle H_2O/H^+} \quad CH_3\overset{\displaystyle OH}{\underset{\displaystyle H}{C}}COOH$$

2 – hydroxypropanoic acid
(lactic acid)

Addition–elimination with 2,4-dinitrophenylhydrazine

Carbonyl compounds undergo a wide range of reactions with nucleophiles containing nitrogen. In the nineteenth century, hydrazine (H_2NNH_2) was found to give crystalline derivatives (hydrazones) with carbonyl compounds, but these derivatives were unsuitable for the identification of the carbonyl compound because their melting points were often indefinite. Their reactions were complicated because either or both nitrogen atoms could react. The use of phenylhydrazine ($C_6H_5NHNH_2$) and its 2,4-dinitro derivative, however, was very successful.

2,4-Dinitrophenylhydrazine, sometimes called Brady's reagent, was particularly useful because the derivatives it gave with carbonyl compounds had low solubility in many solvents, and the formation of an orange precipitate could be used as a simple test for the presence of a carbonyl group.

Nucleophilic attack by the unsubstituted :NH_2 group gives an unstable addition product:

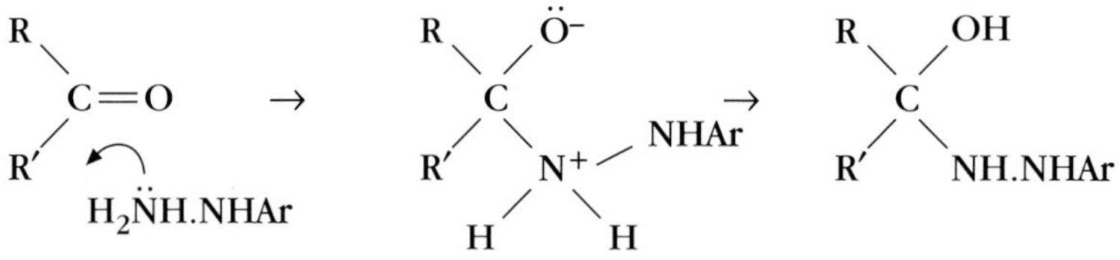

This rapidly loses water to form a hydrazone:

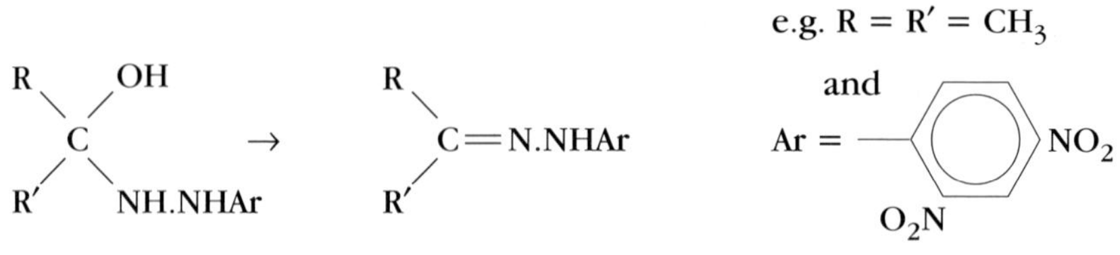

e.g. R = R′ = CH_3
and
Ar =

Carboxylic acids and esters

Introduction

The carboxylic acids are liquids or low-melting solids (Table 1.3). The lower members are soluble in water and smell vinegary. Two common ones are methanoic acid (H.COOH), in nettle stings and ant bites, and ethanoic acid (CH_3COOH), in vinegar.

Table 1.2 *Melting and boiling points of aliphatic carboxylic acids*

Formula	Name	M.p./°C	B.p./°C
HCOOH	methanoic acid	8	101
CH_3COOH	ethanoic acid	17	118
C_2H_5COOH	propanoic acid	−20	141
C_3H_7COOH	butanoic acid	−8	163

They owe both their low volatility and their solubility in water to hydrogen-bonding. This tends to give rise to dimers in the pure acid (Figure 1.8), and accounts for the unusually high melting point of ethanoic acid when compared with other two-carbon atoms compounds.

Hydrogen-bonding between water and acid   Hydrogen-bonded dimer in the solid state

Figure 1.8 Hydrogen-bonding in aqueous solutions of carboxylic acids and dimer formation

The acids may be made by the oxidation of primary alcohols, haloform oxidation of methyl ketones, etc. (page 7), the hydrolysis of amides and cyanides (page 26), the hydrolysis of esters (page 12) and by using Grignard reagents (page 18). Aromatic carboxylic acids may also be made by the oxidation of side-chains (page 19).

Acid properties of carboxylic acids

The carboxylic acids are weaker than mineral acids, e.g. H_2SO_4, but stronger than ethanol or water, which also contain the —O—H link. This is because, when loss of a proton (H^+) occurs, the negative charge on the oxygen is not delocalised in water and ethanol, and the electronegativity of carbon is not so great as the electronegativity of sulphur. Thus the stability of the anions decreases in the order

$$
\underset{HO}{\overset{O}{\underset{}{\diagdown}}}\overset{\overset{O}{\diagup}}{\underset{}{S}}\underset{:O^-}{\overset{}{\diagup}} \quad etc. > \quad R-C\overset{O}{\underset{:O^-}{\diagdown}} \quad > \quad R-O^-
$$

They form the usual range of inorganic salts. Salts of the alkali metals and ammonia are soluble in water. The sodium and potassium salts of the higher carboxylic acids, e.g. octadecanoic (stearic) and hexadecanoic (palmitic), find use as soaps (page), and the lithium salts are employed in engineering as greases.

Esters are formed by heating the acids with alcohols in the presence of a catalyst, usually concentrated sulphuric acid:

$$
ROH \ + \ R'CO_2H \ \overset{H^+}{\rightleftharpoons} \ R'CO_2R \ + \ H_2O
$$

As the esters can no longer have intermolecular hydrogen-bonding, they are more volatile than the acids (and possibly more volatile than the alcohols from which they were made) unless the alkyl group R is very large in comparison with the group R'. Thus the esters can often be separated from the reaction mixture by continuous distillation, which drives the equilibrium to the right.

Esters are employed in food flavourings, perfumes and cosmetics, solvents for glues, varnishes and spray-paints. The alkaline hydrolysis of esters, called 'saponification', is the basis of soap manufacture. Because the acid species is in the anionic form (as a salt), the alkaline hydrolysis, unlike the acid hydrolysis, is irreversible and does not reach equilibrium. Esters of propane-1,2,3-triol (glycerol) occur naturally as oils, fats and waxes.

Whilst acids ionise and form salts by fission of the —O—H bond, esters are formed and hydrolysed by breaking and making the adjacent C—O bond. The group RC=O is known as an acyl group, and this mechanism is accordingly known as acyl-oxygen fission:

$$
\underset{HO^-:}{\overset{O}{\underset{}{R-C-OR'}}} \ \rightleftharpoons \ \underset{HO \quad H-OH}{\overset{O:}{\underset{}{R-C-OR'}}} \ \rightleftharpoons \ \underset{HO \quad + \ :OH^-}{\overset{O}{\underset{}{R-C}}} + R'OH
$$

Halogen derivatives of carboxylic acids

Acids can form two types of halogen derivative. Treatment with chlorine (bromine and iodine are slightly more difficult) in ultra-violet light or sunlight brings about homolytic substitution in the alkane chain at the 2-position (or α-position):

$$CH_3CH_2CO_2H \quad + \quad Cl_2 \quad \xrightarrow{heat} \quad CH_3CHClCO_2H \quad + \quad HCl$$
$$\text{2-chloropropanoic acid}$$

These acids are useful intermediates in the preparation of amino acids and hydroxy acids (see Haloalkanes pages 14 and 16), e.g.

$$CH_3CHClCO_2H \quad + \quad NaOH \quad \rightarrow \quad CH_3CH(OH)CO_2H \quad + \quad NaCl$$
$$\text{2-chloropropanoic acid} \qquad\qquad \text{2-hydroxypropanoic acid}$$
$$\text{(lactic acid)}$$

Phosphorus pentachloride replaces —OH with —Cl to give acyl chlorides:

$$RCOOH \quad + \quad PCl_5 \quad \rightarrow \quad RCOCl \quad + \quad HCl \quad + \quad POCl_3$$

In these very useful intermediates, the activity of the acyl group towards nucleophiles has been enhanced by the presence of the chlorine atom.

Acyl halides form esters with alcohols, amides with ammonia, and secondary amides with amines, e.g.

$$CH_3COCl \quad + \quad C_2H_5OH \quad \rightarrow \quad C_2H_5O_2CCH_3 \quad + \quad HCl$$
$$\text{ethyl ethanoate}$$

$$CH_3COCl \quad + \quad 2NH_3 \quad \rightarrow \quad CH_3CONH_2 \quad + \quad NH_4Cl$$
$$\text{ethanamide}$$

$$CH_3COCl \quad + \quad C_6H_5NH_2 \quad \rightarrow \quad C_6H_5NHCOCH_3 \quad + \quad HCl$$
$$\textit{N}\text{-phenylethanamide}$$

They are hydrolysed in the presence of water (faster in alkali) to give the acid (or salt):

$$CH_3COCl \quad + \quad 2NaOH \quad \rightarrow \quad CH_3COONa \quad + \quad NaCl \quad + \quad H_2O$$

Acyl halides are unpleasant, lachrymatory liquids, and the above reaction is often a useful way of removing excess of them from reaction mixtures.

Why should replacing OH with Cl make acid chlorides more reactive than acids towards nucleophiles?

THE CHEMISTRY OF ORGANIC COMPOUNDS
Haloalkanes (alkyl halides)

Introduction
The preparation of these compounds by homolytic substitution, addition to alkenes and displacement of —OH has already been met.

The main usefulness of the haloalkanes lies in their ability to undergo nucleophilic substitution and replacement of the halogen, e.g.

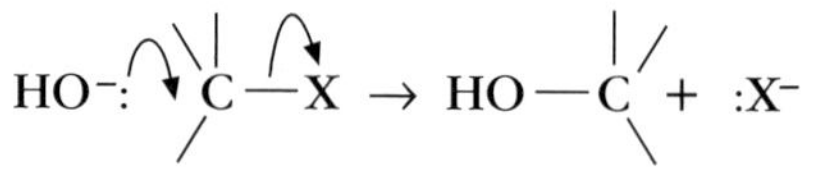

$$HO^- : \quad C-X \rightarrow HO-C + :X^-$$

You must always remember that this is a functional group property and that it applies equally to compounds like α-chloroacids.

Elimination or substitution? Alcohols or alkenes?
In *Principles of Physical and Organic Chemistry* you may have been struck by the difference that a change of solvent makes to the reaction of potassium hydroxide on haloalkanes:

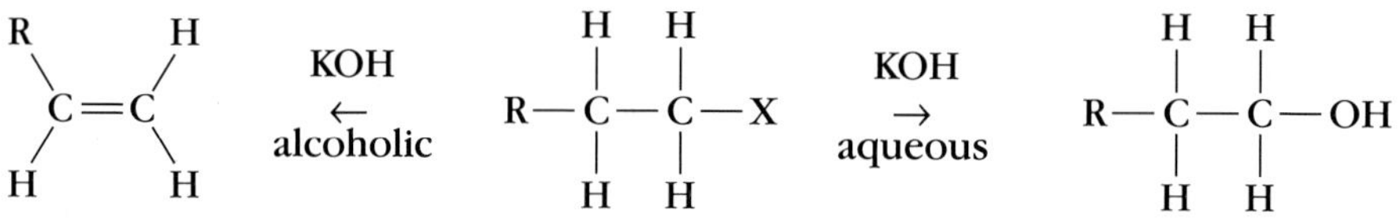

alkene   ← KOH alcoholic   haloalkane   KOH aqueous →   alcohol

Unfortunately it isn't quite that simple!

Alternative reactions often compete in organic chemistry and give different products. The yields of desired products are often low, and the presence of a mixture of products (and unchanged starting material) often results in further losses during purification. The organic chemist often has to choose conditions with care in order to influence one path or the other. The dominance of substitution or elimination depends on the choice of nucleophile, the halide and the reaction conditions.

Reaction of haloalkanes with cyanide ion
The cyanide ion acts as an effective nucleophile and displaces the halogen, e.g.

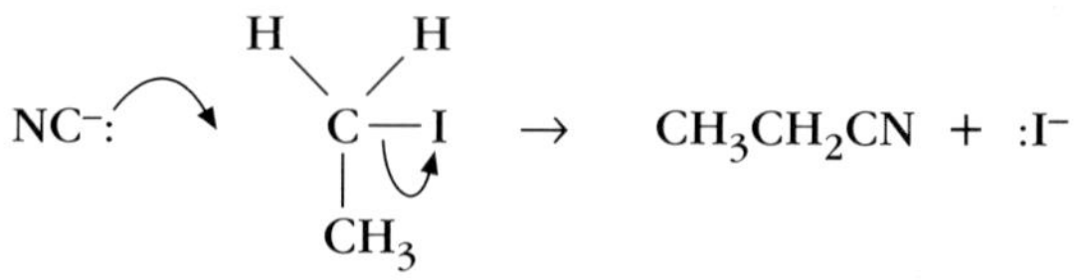

$$NC^- : \quad C-I \rightarrow CH_3CH_2CN + :I^-$$

14

The naming of the resulting compounds is a little difficult, because at various times several different systems have been in use.

- If the cyanide group is the terminal grouping and could be considered to extend the carbon chain, it is named as a **nitrile**: in such cases its carbon atom is included in the total count of carbon atoms. For example, CH_3CN is ethanenitrile.

- If the cyanide group does not extend a chain, then it is named as a substituent 'cyano'. For example, C_6H_5CN is cyanobenzene (cf. chlorobenzene).

Older names that persist for these two compounds are acetonitrile and benzonitrile.

For the preparation of nitriles (cyanides), alcoholic potassium cyanide is used. Aqueous potassium or sodium cyanide is unsuitable because hydrolysis occurs:

$$:CN^- \; + \; H_2O \; \rightarrow \; HCN \; + \; :OH^-$$

The hydroxide ion then tends to give alcohols (substitution) or alkenes (elimination) instead of the desired product.

Nitriles are important synthetically because the introduction of the CN group allows extension of the carbon chain to produce a higher homologue. With this aim, the cyanide group may be either hydrolysed or reduced.

Hydrolysis is brought about by boiling with either aqueous acid or alkali. It is not always possible to stop the hydrolysis at the amide stage. If this product is desired, it might well be better to complete the hydrolysis and then make the ammonium salt and eliminate water (see below and page 25):

$$RCN \; \xrightarrow{H_2O/H^+} \; RCONH_2 \; \xrightarrow{H_2O/H^+} \; RCO_2^-NH_4^+$$

Although the ammonium salt is shown as the theoretical product, it is never obtained. If acid hydrolysis, e.g. moderately concentrated sulphuric acid, is used, then the ammonium salt of the strong acid, e.g. ammonium sulphate, is obtained. If alkaline hydrolysis is used, e.g. aqueous sodium hydroxide, then the sodium salt of the organic acid is formed and ammonia is expelled.

Reduction (of nitriles) can be brought about by a range of materials from catalytic hydrogenation to lithium aluminium hydride and gives rise to primary amines

$$RCN \; \xrightarrow{H_2/Ni} \; RCH_2NH_2$$

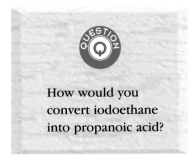

How would you convert iodoethane into propanoic acid?

How would you convert iodoethane into propylamine?

Reaction of haloalkanes with ammonia

The reaction

$$RI + NH_3 \rightarrow RNH_2 + HI$$

to prepare the corresponding primary amine (cf. the higher homologue via cyanide above) is beset with problems.

Because ammonia is gaseous and the reaction requires heat, it needs to be done under pressure in a sealed apparatus (autoclave or sealed tube). The chemist cannot take advantage of the greater solubility of ammonia in water than in the more volatile ethanol (which needs higher working pressures for the same temperature). This is because, in water, the ammonia will give rise to appreciable amounts of hydroxide ion, which will compete as a nucleophile:

$$:NH_3 + H_2O \rightleftharpoons NH_4^+ + :OH^-$$

As soon as the first organic molecules have started to react, the initial product, a primary amine, then acts as a competing nucleophile, which would give a secondary amine:

$$RNH_2 + RI \rightarrow R_2NH + HI$$

This undesirable step both loses product and loses fresh starting material in one reaction. It can be overcome by using large excesses of ammonia, which must be employed in any case because one of the products, HI, will remove an equimolar amount of ammonia:

$$NH_3 + HI \rightarrow NH_4I$$

The greater the amount of excess ammonia, the more unpleasant is the isolation and purification stage.

Choice of halides in synthesis

Iodides are preferred to bromides; chlorides are seldom used. This preference stems from two causes.

- The reactivity of the haloalkanes is directly linked to the relative activity of the C—X group. The C—X bond is more highly polarised in chlorides than iodides, and it might at first appear that it might be more reactive. In iodides, however, the much greater radius of the iodine atom and great bond length of C—I allows greater polarisation of the bond by the approaching nucleophile, and it is this which controls the reaction ultimately.

- The activation energy of all organic reactions is appreciable since covalent bonds normally have to be broken, at least partially, to arrive at the transition state. Most organic reactions have to be heated to achieve an acceptable rate. The higher boiling point of the iodides means that reaction mixtures can be boiled under reflux at higher temperatures and that any escaping haloalkane is likely to be condensed and returned to the reaction flask.

Organometallic compounds

Introduction

A big step forward in chemistry was made at the end of the nineteenth century, by chemists such as Frankland and Grignard (Figures 1.9 and 1.10), when the synthetic potential of organometallic compounds was first revealed. An organometallic compound is one in which a metal is linked to a carbon atom by a bond with significant covalent character.

There will always be some ionic character to the metal–carbon bond because the electronegativities of metals are less than that of carbon. A most important feature of this ionic character is that the carbon, unusually, carries a partial negative charge, i.e. it is not a carbocation but a carbanion.

Figure 1.9 Francois Grignard (1871–1935)

Grignard reagents

Grignard found that haloalkanes would dissolve magnesium in the presence of dry ethoxyethane (ether) when they were heated together under reflux:

$$C_2H_5I \quad + \quad Mg \quad \xrightarrow{\text{dry ether}} \quad C_2H_5MgI$$

The ether must be perfectly dry since moisture destroys the resulting **Grignard reagents**:

$$C_2H_5MgI \quad + \quad H_2O \quad \rightarrow \quad C_2H_6 \quad + \quad \text{`Mg(OH)I'}$$

Formulae like Mg(OH)I are used as a convenience in organic chemistry – just as Al^{3+} or $AlCl_3$(aq) may be used in inorganic chemistry instead of $[Al(H_2O)_6]^{3+}$(aq) when we do not wish to labour some point about that aspect of the chemistry. It is not truly representative of what is formed, but correctly represents the stoichiometry.

A trace of iodine helps to initiate the reaction, and the choice of solvent is crucial. The ether, $C_2H_5OC_2H_5$, helps to stabilise the organometallic complex by solvating the combined magnesium, in a similar way to that in which the solvation energy of the sodium and chloride ions allows crystalline sodium chloride to dissolve in water. The Grignard reagents are always used *in situ*.

Figure 1.10 Percy Frankland (1858–1946)

Reactions and synthetic importance of Grignard reagents

The unusual role of carbon as a carbanion (see above) makes it act as a nucleophile. When looking at how these reagents behave, it is difficult to represent the polarity of the Mg—C bond when the link between the Mg atom and the ion of X is ionic. Structures like that in Figure 1.11a are undoubtedly more accurate than that in Figure 1.11b because the second structure fails to show the ionic nature of the halide bond. However, the latter is the more usual representation of the structure.

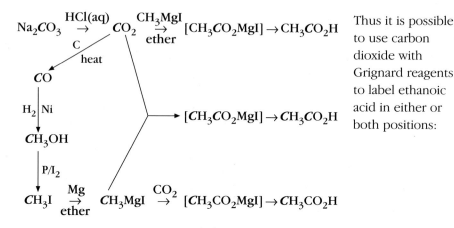

Figure 1.11 *Charge distribution in a Grignard reagent*

Reactions with aldehydes and ketones

Nucleophilic addition to an aldehyde or ketone and decomposition of the resulting complex with dilute acid gives secondary or tertiary alcohols, respectively:

Show how tertiary alcohols are formed from ketones by a similar mechanism.

The complex could be hydrolysed by water alone, but the resulting suspension of magnesium hydroxide and basic magnesium salts would be far less pleasant to deal with than a solution.

Reaction with carbon dioxide

The addition of a Grignard reagent to carbon dioxide is a convenient method of extending a carbon chain:

Apart from its use as a rather expensive general synthetic method, this reaction has proved of enormous value in preparing carboxylic acids labelled with carbon-14 (^{14}C) for the purpose of radio-tracing, both *in vitro* and *in vivo*. One of the most convenient forms of commercially available ^{14}C is ^{14}C-labelled sodium carbonate: this is ideal for the generation of ^{14}C-enriched carbon dioxide.

In vitro and in vivo
In vitro literally means 'in glassware', i.e. on the bench
In vivo means 'in a living organism'

$$Na_2CO_3 \xrightarrow[C]{HCl(aq)} CO_2 \xrightarrow[ether]{CH_3MgI} [CH_3CO_2MgI] \rightarrow CH_3CO_2H$$

Thus it is possible to use carbon dioxide with Grignard reagents to label ethanoic acid in either or both positions:

$$CO_2 \xrightarrow[heat]{} CO$$

$$CO \xrightarrow{H_2|Ni} CH_3OH$$

$$[CH_3CO_2MgI] \rightarrow CH_3CO_2H$$

$$CH_3OH \xrightarrow{P/I_2} CH_3I \xrightarrow[ether]{Mg} CH_3MgI \xrightarrow{CO_2} [CH_3CO_2MgI] \rightarrow CH_3CO_2H$$

The chemistry of aromatic compounds

Introduction

You met aromatic compounds in *Principles of Physical and Organic Chemistry*. Aromatic compounds are those, like benzene, whose structures contain aromatic ring systems, which appear to be unsaturated but which do not easily undergo the addition reactions typical of unsaturated compounds.

Benzenoid compounds are named either as if the benzene ring is a substituent in another structure when it is referred to as phenyl, e.g. 4-phenylbutanal $C_6H_5CH_2CH_2CH_2CHO$, or as substituted benzene, e.g. chlorobenzene C_6H_5Cl.

The reactions of aromatic compounds can be divided into two types: those of the aromatic ring and those of the aliphatic side-chain. The reactions of the aromatic ring, unless they are homolytic reactions brought about under extreme conditions, are electrophilic substitutions. The side-chain reactions are essentially those of the compounds that you have met so far, though the relative reactivity may be changed by the proximity of the benzene ring. There is one important exception to this generalisation, which we shall deal with first.

Side-chain oxidation

Gentle side-chain oxidation achieves the same results as in the aliphatic compounds. Thus acidified dichromate will oxidise 2-phenylethanol (**A**) first to phenylethanal (**B**) and then to phenylethanoic acid (**C**). The group C_6H_5— is often symbolised as Ph— (even if the compound is named ...-obenzene):

$$\text{PhCH}_2\text{CH}_2\text{OH} \rightarrow \text{PhCH}_2\text{CHO} \rightarrow \text{PhCH}_2\text{CO}_2\text{H}$$
$$\qquad\text{A}\qquad\qquad\qquad\text{B}\qquad\qquad\qquad\text{C}$$

Similarly phenylpropan-2-ol (**D**) would be oxidised to phenylpropanone (**E**), which, in turn, could be oxidised by the haloform reaction to phenylethanoic acid (**C**) and triiodomethane CHI_3:

$$\text{PhCH}_2\text{CH(OH)CH}_3 \rightarrow \text{PhCH}_2\text{COCH}_3 \rightarrow \text{PhCH}_2\text{CO}_2\text{H}$$
$$\qquad\quad\text{D}\qquad\qquad\qquad\qquad\text{E}\qquad\qquad\qquad\text{C}$$

Hot potassium manganate(VII) solution oxidises all side-chains *in which carbon is directly linked to the benzene ring* to a carboxyl group —COOH. The reagent may be used in acidic, alkaline or neutral solution. Thus, all five of the compounds **A**–**E** above would be oxidised to benzenecarboxylic acid (benzoic acid) PhCOOH. This reaction is of greater diagnostic than preparative use. A benzene derivative, on oxidation with hot acidified manganate(VII), will give a mono-, di- or tri- (etc.) carboxylic acid, which will be easily recognised as such, both by its analysis (formula is $[C_6H_6 + nCO_2]$ where n is the number of carboxylic acid groups: $C_7H_6O_2$ = mono-, $C_8H_6O_4$ = di-, $C_9H_6O_6$ = tricarboxylic acid), and also by its melting point (and mixed melting point) or infra-red spectrum. Correct identification of a benzenedicarboxylic or -tricarboxylic acid will give immediate information on the number and relative positions of the side-chains that have been oxidised. Benzene-1,2-dicarboxylic acid may also be recognised because it loses water very easily on heating:

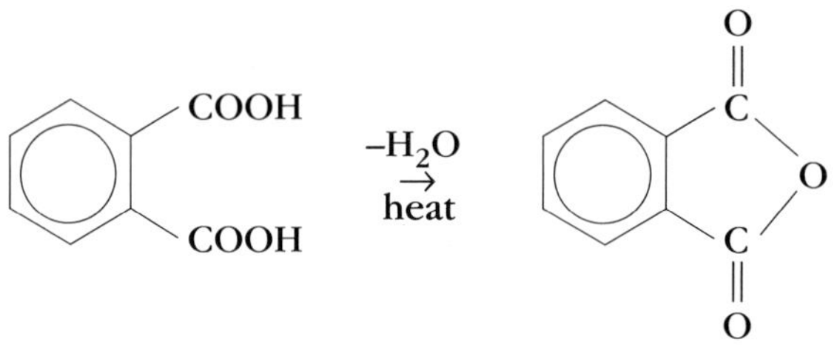

Addition reactions of the aromatic ring

In extreme conditions, such as treatment of boiling benzene with chlorine in ultra-violet light or catalytic high-pressure hydrogenation, addition reactions can be made to occur:

$$C_6H_6 + 3Cl_2 \rightarrow C_6H_6Cl_6$$

$$C_6H_6 + 3H_2 \rightarrow C_6H_{12}$$

However, the normal reaction of the aromatic nucleus is electrophilic substitution.

Creating side-chains

Direct introduction of a side-chain by a C—C link with the nucleus is made possible by the Friedel–Crafts reaction, named after its discoverers. They succeeded by mixing a halogeno compound (usually chloro) with anhydrous aluminium chloride. The anhydrous aluminium chloride acts as a lone-pair acceptor towards the halide (Figure 1.12).

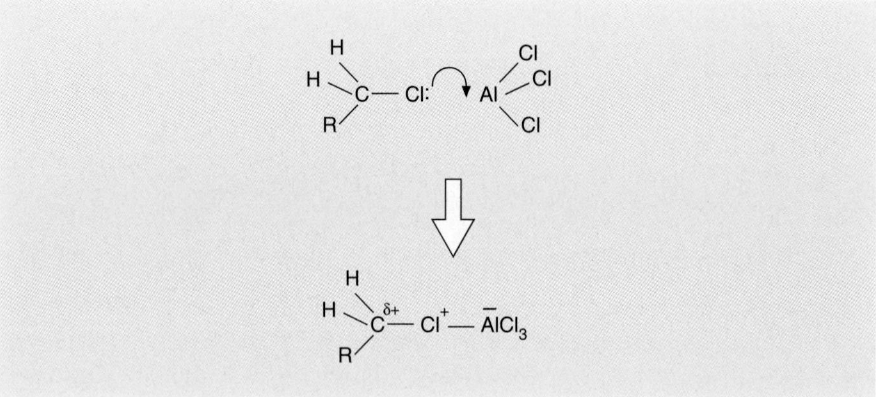

Figure 1.12 Formation of adduct between RX and AlX$_3$

The positive charge generated on the chlorine atom has the effect of pulling the electrons away from the carbon in the C—Cl bond, which makes this **C** atom an effective electrophile (or, alternatively, makes it very susceptible to nucleophilic attack by the π-electrons of the benzene ring). The complex reacts with the benzene ring and introduces a side-chain:

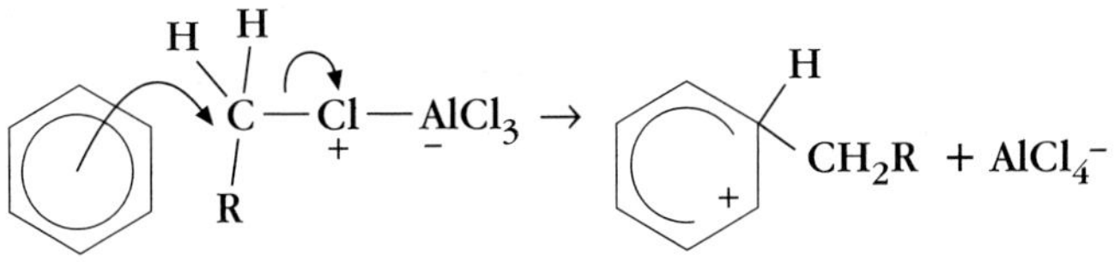

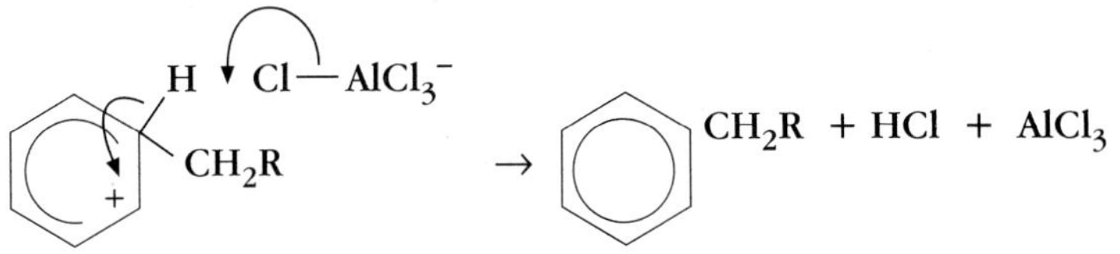

The reaction is not confined to haloalkanes, and a very useful side-chain to introduce is an acyl group since it gives a carbonyl group next to the benzene ring. This can then be used for further synthetic steps (e.g. with Grignard reagents):

$$C_6H_6 \ + \ RCOCl \ \xrightarrow{AlCl_3} \ C_6H_5COR \ + \ HCl$$

Nitration

Nitration has been fully explained (*Principles of Physical and Organic Chemistry*, page 106). It is the most common method of introducing direct nitrogen links into the aromatic nucleus.

The resulting nitro compounds are of enormous industrial importance as intermediates in the manufacture of aromatic amines. They are, themselves, the basis of some explosives, an important example of which is TNT.

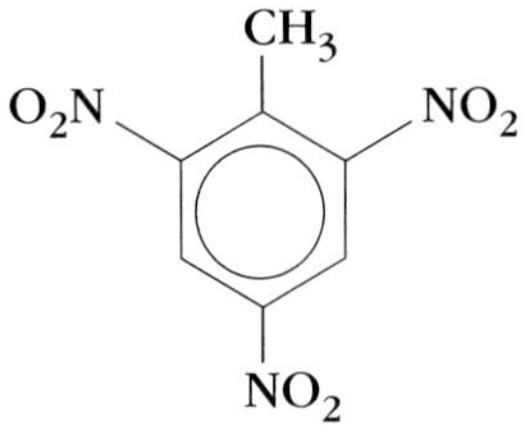

TNT

Amines

Introduction

We have already met two methods of making aliphatic amines. Nucleophilic substitution in haloalkanes (page 16) and reduction of nitriles (page 15). We shall meet another when we come to amides. As indicated above, a different method is used for the preparation of aromatic amines. Before we look at their general chemistry, let us examine this method of preparation.

Preparation of aromatic amines

The reduction of aromatic nitro compounds is the usual route to aromatic amines. This route is, in theory, applicable to aliphatic nitro compounds, but these are not so easy to make, and there are many easier routes such as nucleophilic substitution by ammonia, reduction of cyanides or the Hofmann degradation (page 26).

Aromatic nuclear chloro compounds are unreactive to nucleophiles like OH^- and ammonia. The interaction of the π-electrons with an unshared pair on the chlorine increases the bond order and strength of the C—Cl bond. Thus simple substitution of chlorobenzene (Figure 1.13) by ammonia is not possible.

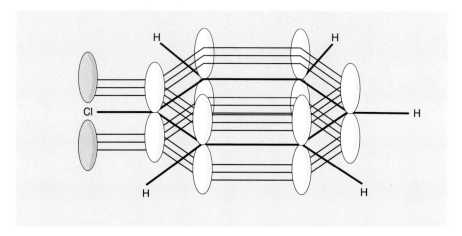

Figure 1.13 Orbital overlap in chlorobenzene

Aromatic nitro compounds can give rise to a wide variety of different reduction products: the method of reduction must be chosen with some care. The traditional laboratory reductant is tin and concentrated hydrochloric acid:

$$C_6H_5NO_2 \;+\; 6H^+ \;+\; 6e^- \;\rightarrow\; C_6H_5NH_2 \;+\; 2H_2O$$

Since amines are basic, it might be considered better to show the formation of the protonated form of the product:

$$C_6H_5NO_2 \;+\; 7H^+ \;+\; 6e^- \;\rightarrow\; C_6H_5NH_3^+ \;+\; 2H_2O$$

with

$$Sn \;+\; 6Cl^- \;\rightarrow\; SnCl_6^{2-} \;+\; 4e^-$$

showing that, to balance the overall equation, 3 mol of tin ($= 12e^-$) are required for 2 mol of nitrobenzene.

Not only is tin a relatively expensive metal (and its large atomic mass means that a lot is required) but also large quantities of alkali are needed to neutralise the large amount of concentrated acid used before the amine is released from the complex hexachlorostannate formed, $C_6H_5NH_3^+HSnCl_6^-$. The method is unsuitable industrially for economic reasons, and nitrobenzene is reduced by iron and water containing just enough hydrochloric acid to achieve a satisfactory reduction:

$$Fe \;+\; 3H_2O \;\rightarrow\; Fe(OH)_3 \;+\; 3H^+ \;+\; 3e^-$$

The chemistry of amines

Methylamine is a gas at room temperature, but the majority of the lower amines are liquids (Table 1.4). They are less volatile than the corresponding alkanes (which are attracted only by the weakest van der Waals forces) or the halides (which have permanent dipoles) because the amines are hydrogen-bonded (Figure 1.14). However, the lower amines are more volatile than the alcohols or the amides (page 25), which are more strongly or extensively hydrogen-bonded.

Hydrogen-bonding in amines

Hydrogen-bonding between water and amines

Figure 1.14 Hydrogen-bonding in amines and between amines and water

Table 1.4 *Boiling points of aliphatic primary amines*

Formula	Name	B.p./°C
CH_3NH_2	methylamine	−6
$C_2H_5NH_2$	ethylamine	17
$C_3H_7NH_2$	propylamine	49
$C_4H_9NH_2$	butylamine	76

The amines have unpleasant smells, which change from ammoniacal to fishy as the molecular mass increases. The lower amines are soluble in water because hydrogen-bonding occurs between the amino group and the water (Figure 1.14).

All amines are basic. The aliphatic amines are slightly more basic than ammonia because of the small positive inductive effect of the alkyl group, but the pH of saturated aqueous solutions falls as the molecular mass increases because of decreasing solubility. Aromatic amines are much less basic and much less soluble in water. The lone pair (p-orbital) on the nitrogen atom interacts with the π-electron system of the benzene ring (Figure 1.15) and is thus less easily protonated.

All the amines form water-soluble salts with mineral acids (HCl, H_2SO_4, etc.):

$$C_6H_5NH_2 \;+\; HCl \;\rightleftharpoons\; C_6H_5NH_3^+Cl^-$$

phenylamine   phenylammonium chloride

(aniline)   (aniline hydrochloride)

Thus amines that are reluctant to dissolve in water form solutions in acids and are reprecipitated by alkalis:

$$\underset{OH^-(aq)}{\overset{H^+(aq)}{C_6H_5NH_2(l) \;\rightleftharpoons\; C_6H_5NH_3^+(aq)}}$$

sparingly   appreciably

soluble   soluble

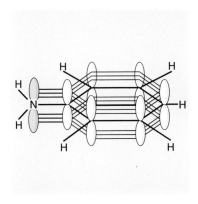

Figure 1.15 Orbital overlap in phenylamine

THE CHEMISTRY OF ORGANIC COMPOUNDS

The simple salts, which are a convenient means of marketing amines, are not suitable for the identification of amines by melting point since they invariably decompose before melting. The most accessible stable covalent derivatives are prepared by treatment with an acyl halide (usually ethanoyl chloride, CH_3COCl, or benzoyl chloride, C_6H_5COCl) or an acid anhydride:

$$C_6H_5NH_2 \; + \; CH_3COCl \; \rightleftharpoons \; C_6H_5NHCOCH_3 \; + \; HCl$$
$$\text{\textit{N}-phenylethanamide}$$

These substituted amides are sometimes used as pharmaceuticals, e.g. paracetamol.

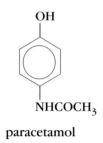

paracetamol

Amines and nitrous acid (HNO_2)

A solution of sodium nitrite (sodium nitrate(III)) in dilute acid gives the unstable, pale blue nitrous acid or nitric(III) acid, HNO_2. This reacts differently with aliphatic and aromatic primary amines.

With aliphatic amines, very poor yields of alcohols are obtained:

$$RNH_2 \; + \; HNO_2 \; \rightleftharpoons \; ROH \; + \; N_2 \; + \; H_2O$$

The reaction is a simple diagnostic test for primary (aliphatic) amines, though the observation of a colourless gas with negative identification tests is not one to inspire confidence.

For aromatic amines, the reaction can be halted at an intermediate diazonium ion:

$$ArNH_2 \; + \; HNO_2 \; + \; HCl \; \rightleftharpoons \; ArN_2{}^+Cl^- \; + \; 2H_2O$$

phenol

In order to make use of this intermediate, it must be prepared at below 5°C and in the presence of excess acid. As it is prepared in aqueous solution, this temperature requirement is particularly easy to satisfy by simply adding ice. The low temperature gives it kinetic stability and the excess acid, amongst other things, prevents it reacting with unchanged amine. It is used *in situ* as soon as possible: on standing, or if the temperature rises, it decomposes to give a poor yield of a phenol (cf. the aliphatic reaction):

$$ArN_2{}^+Cl^- \; + \; H_2O \; \rightleftharpoons \; ArOH \; + \; N_2 \; + \; HCl$$
$$\text{a phenol}$$

The diazonium ion is an electrophile and condenses with phenols and aromatic amines to give highly coloured compounds. Phenols are nuclear-substituted aromatic hydroxy compounds. The amines employed are usually tertiary in order to prevent the electrophile (El) from attacking the lone pair of the nitrogen, and displacing a proton:

The initial formation of the diazonium ion is called **diazotisation**. The subsequent reaction with the aromatic amine or phenol is called **coupling**:

$$C_6H_5-\overset{+}{N}\equiv N + \text{(phenol)}-OH \rightarrow C_6H_5-N=N-\text{(phenyl)}-OH + H^+$$

A minor use of the reaction is as a test for aromatic primary amines. An attempt is made to diazotise the suspected primary amine and an alkaline solution of 2-naphthol is added to the mixture. A positive result is the formation of a highly coloured precipitate, usually red:

aromatic diazonium chloride

red precipitate

The main use of the reaction is to produce synthetic dyes and some acid–base indicators.

Explain why this test cannot be used for the detection of a tertiary amine.

Amides

Introduction

Amides are acyl derivatives of ammonia. With the exception of methanamide, they are solids (Table 1.5), and the lower members are all soluble in water. Both these properties are caused by hydrogen-bonding (Figure 1.16). The ability to form dimers gives the amides their relatively high melting points.

As we have seen, they can be made by the action of ammonia on acyl halides. Acyl halides are normally made from the acids, and a cheaper route to the amides is thermal dehydration of the ammonium salt of the acid:

$$R-C\overset{O}{\underset{O^-NH_4^+}{}} \xrightarrow{\text{heat}} R-C\overset{O}{\underset{NH_2}{}} + H_2O$$

This reaction, as happens so often in organic chemistry, is in competition with thermal loss of ammonia:

$$R-C\overset{O}{\underset{O^-NH_4^+}{}} \xrightarrow{\text{heat}} R-C\overset{O}{\underset{OH}{}} + NH_3$$

If a high yield from the acid is required, the route via the acyl halide may be preferred. Esters also react with ammonia to give amides, but the reaction is of less significance.

Whilst the hydrolysis of cyanides (page 15) gives first an amide and then a carboxylic acid, it is seldom possible to stop at the intermediate amide.

Table 1.5 *Melting points of aliphatic amines*

Formula	Name	M.p./°C
$HCONH_2$	methanamide	3
CH_3CONH_2	ethanamide	82
$C_2H_5CONH_2$	propanamide	81
C_3H_7CONH	butanamide	115

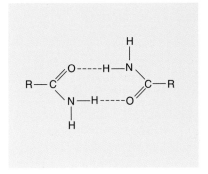

Figure 1.16 Intermolecular hydrogen-bonding in amides

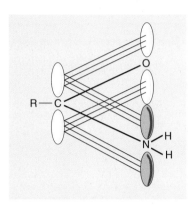

Figure 1.17 Orbital overlap in amides

The chemistry of amides

Unlike amines, amides are not appreciably basic: their aqueous solutions are neutral. The lone pair of electrons on the nitrogen atom, which is responsible for base character, is made less available by interaction with the π-system of the carbonyl group (Figure 1.17). The reduction in base character of the aromatic amines compared with the aliphatic amines (page 23) is due to a similar cause, but the electronegativity of the oxygen atom makes the carbonyl group far more effective than the benzene ring.

At the same time, the effect of the oxygen atom in creating a positive charge on the C of the carbonyl group is reduced. Thus amides, like acids and esters, do not undergo the nucleophilic addition reactions of aldehydes and ketones with, for example, cyanide.

Hofmann degradation of amides

Amides have little synthetic value as intermediates, but sometimes they can be used as a means of introducing the amino group —NH_2 with the simultaneous loss of a carbon atom. This reaction is known as the Hofmann degradation: a degradation implies the loss of a carbon atom from a molecule. It is brought about by the action of bromine and sodium hydroxide:

$$RCONH_2 + Br_2 + 2NaOH \rightarrow RNH_2 + CO_2 + 2NaBr + 2H_2O$$

Hydration and dehydration

It has been seen that amides are intermediates in the dehydration of ammonium salts to nitriles (cyanides) and the hydration of nitriles to carboxylic acids. Whilst it is often difficult to stop the hydration of cyanides at the amide stage

$$\underset{\text{nitrile}}{RCN} \rightarrow \underset{\text{amide}}{RCONH_2} \rightarrow \underset{\text{carboxylic acid}}{RCO_2H} \quad (+ NH_3 \quad \text{or} \quad NH_4^+)$$

the thermal dehydration of ammonium salts goes no further than the amide

$$RCO_2^-NH_4^+ \rightarrow RCONH_2 + H_2O$$

The amide can, however be dehydrated by heating with phosphorus(v) oxide, P_4O_{10}:

$$RCONH_2 \overset{P_4O_{10}}{\underset{-H_2O}{\rightarrow}} RCN$$

Thus it can be seen that an amide can be converted into an amine with either the same number of carbon atoms or one less:

$$RNH_2 \overset{NaOH/Br_2}{\leftarrow} \underset{\text{amide}}{RCONH_2} \overset{P_4O_{10}}{\underset{-H_2O}{\rightarrow}} RCN \overset{H_2/Ni}{\underset{\substack{\text{or other} \\ \text{reduction}}}{\rightarrow}} RCH_2NH_2$$

Suggest a powerful reducing agent that might be able to reduce an amide directly to the amine with the same number of carbon atoms.

2 The commercial importance of organic compounds

Organic chemistry has had an influence in every walk of life. The clothes we wear are often blends of wool or cotton with synthetic fibres such as nylon or terylene. The shoe-repairer, once a feature of every town and village, has all but disappeared with the marketing of 'throw-away' footwear, shoes with hard-wearing synthetic soles and often synthetic uppers as well, probably glued together with a synthetic adhesive.

Polymers have had consequences never dreamt of by Leo Baekeland, inventor of the first modern 'plastic', Bakelite, early in the twentieth century. Their uses range from 'Lego' sets to the interiors of jet air-liners. Some are shown in Figure 2.1.

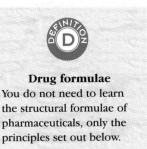

Drug formulae
You do not need to learn the structural formulae of pharmaceuticals, only the principles set out below.

Figure 2.1 Some uses of modern plastics

Pharmaceuticals

Introduction

Two distinct approaches are applied to the synthesis of drugs. Simple drugs like the analgesics aspirin, paracetamol and ibuprofen (Figure 2.2) are purely synthetic. More elaborate pain-killers like morphine and codeine (Figure 2.3), antibiotics like penicillin, or physiologically active hormones are made by biosynthesis and subsequent modification. However, the great benefits of the vast range of modern antibiotics and drugs (Figure 2.4) have been accompanied by the social problems of drug abuse.

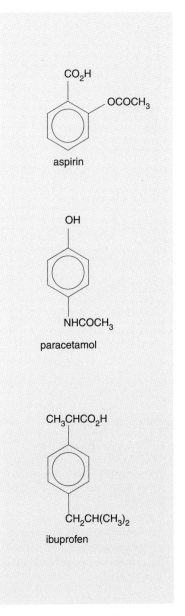

Figure 2.2 The structures of aspirin, paracetamol and ibuprofen

THE COMMERCIAL IMPORTANCE OF ORGANIC COMPOUNDS

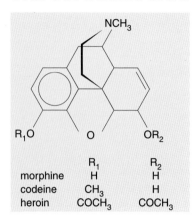

Figure 2.3 The structures of morphine, codeine and heroin

Morphine is extracted from poppy seeds, codeine is made by the chemical modification of morphine, penicillins are made (initially) by mould culture. Great progress is being made in the manufacture of materials like the hormone insulin. Traditionally extracted from an animal pancreas, it can now be made by genetically engineered routes. In such methods, sections of genes from animals are spliced into the genetic material of bacteria, which then produce the required compound as part of their life-cycle.

Scientists are always looking for ways of chemically modifying the structures of pharmaceuticals. One reason is in order to change the solubility and retention time of the material in the body.

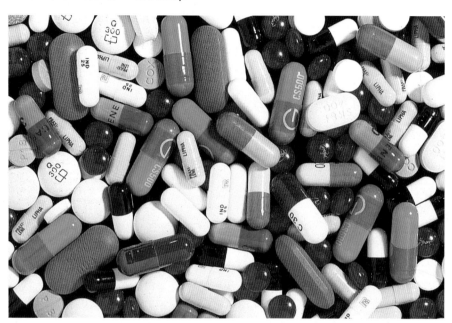

Figure 2.4 Some of the drugs that we take

Solubility and retention time

Solubility in water and the retention time of a drug in the body are related, though only in a most general way. The more soluble a compound is in water, the faster it is likely to be transported to the liver (the most common site for breakdown or biotransformation of the material), and the sooner it or its more soluble oxidation products can be expelled in the urine via the kidneys. The higher the proportion of hydrophilic groups ($-OH$, $-NH_2$, $-CO_2H$, $-CO_2^-$, etc.), the lower the probable retention time because the material tends to be confined to the blood, lymph and aqueous tissue. The more lipophilic groups (e.g. alkyl side-chains $-CH_2CH_2CH_2CH_2CH_2CH_2CH_2CH_3$) there are in the structure, the more likely it is to pass into cellular membranes and fatty tissue with slow release into blood or lymph and the longer is its probable retention time in the body. A balance has to be struck between the two (as well as the other consequences mentioned). If a drug is too lipophilic, it may not be able to achieve sufficient concentration in the bloodstream to be effective or it may not be sufficiently soluble to allow absorption before passing through the gut.

Hydrophilic and lipophilic
Hydrophilic means 'attracted to water'
Hydrophobic means 'not attracted to water' (attracted to fatty materials)
Lipophilic means 'attracted to fatty materials'

The effects of even minor changes of structure on property are quite marked. Aspirin is sufficiently water-soluble to be an effective pain-killer. The much less water-soluble methyl ester, oil of wintergreen (Figure 2.5), is used for external application (in embrocations and rubs), where lipophilic character is desirable if the material is to be absorbed through the skin.

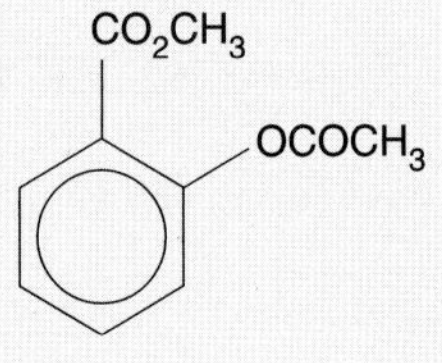

The solubility of aspirin is increased by preparing the sodium or calcium salt. This, however, is merely to facilitate 'taking the aspirin'; soluble aspirin dissolves in water quite easily. Not only is the solubility greater but also the rate at which it dissolves is increased by mixing calcium carbonate and citric acid in the tablet: this rapidly disperses the tablet in (warm) water. The ionic form $—CO_2^-$ is largely converted back to the un-ionised $—CO_2H$ in the acidic conditions of the stomach, but by then the aspirin is in a relatively large volume of liquid at 37°C and the decreased solubility is less important. The low pH in the stomach can, however, represent a serious problem. When a drug is seriously affected by acid, it must either be modified for oral use or be given by injection.

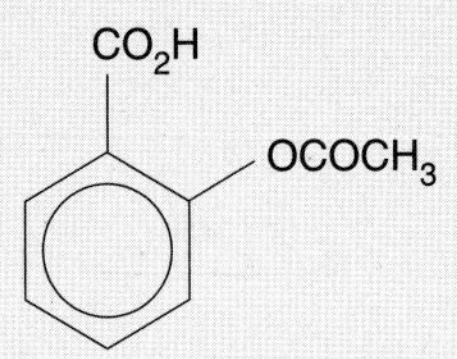

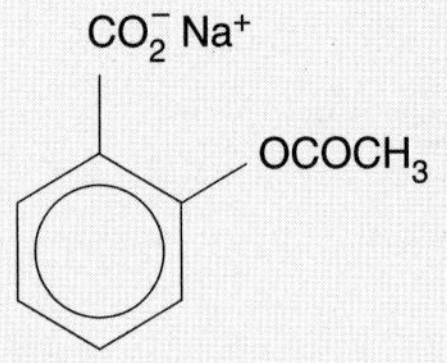

The penicillins are important antibiotics that combat certain types of bacteria by preventing them building cell walls. This does not kill the existing bacteria, but when they attempt to divide they are unable to produce viable off spring. Fortunately, mammalian cells are different – they have cell membranes but no walls around them. Since it was first used, half a century ago, penicillin has been modified hundreds of times and many forms of it are used today.

The original 'penicillin', penicillin G, is extremely water-soluble and rapidly excreted in the urine. During the first clinical trials (in 1941), a policeman's life was one of the first to be saved by its use. It is so soluble, and was in such short supply, that some of the drug had to be recovered from the urine of other patients in order to provide enough.

The solubility in water can be reduced by incorporating lipophilic side-chains. Thus the replacement of the sodium ion by procaine gives a species with much greater retention time.

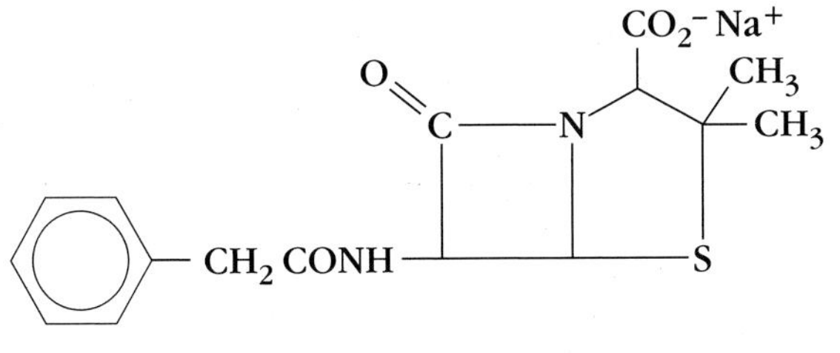

Figure 2.5 Structures of aspirin, its soluble sodium salt and oil of wintergreen

penicillin G

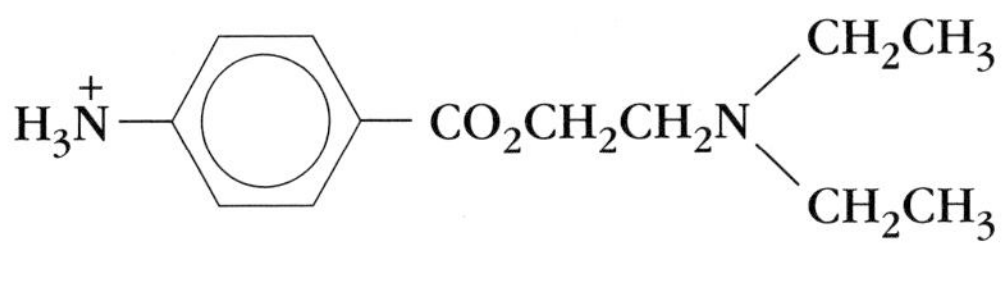

procaine (cation)

In contrast to the need to reduce the hydrophilic character of natural penicillin, it is of first importance that penicillamine (Figure 2.6), a penicillin derivative, is as water-soluble as possible: with two hydrophilic groups and only four carbon atoms per molecule it could hardly be otherwise. This compound's therapeutic use lies in its solubility and the rapidity with which it can be excreted. It is used to form coordination complexes with heavy metals such as copper and lead, e.g. in the case of lead poisoning.

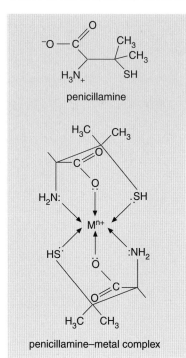

Figure 2.6 Structures of penicillamine and its metal complex

chloramphenicol

Figure 2.7 Ammonium nitrate pellets and the machinery needed to spread them over the field

Another example of a drug, the hydrophilic or lipophilic character of which may be increased or decreased by minor chemical modification, is chloramphenicol. The marked hydrogen atom may be replaced by hexadecanoate (palmitate)

$$-O_2CCH_2CH_2CH_2CH_2CH_2CH_2CH_2CH_2CH_2CH_2CH_2CH_2CH_2CH_2CH_3$$

to lower solubility. (It has a nasty taste and can then be administered by mouth as a fine 'insoluble' suspension to patients who cannot swallow a capsule. It is then hydrolysed to chloramphenicol in the stomach and intestines.) Replacement of the same group by the more hydrophilic $-OCCH_2CH_2CO_2^-Na^+$ renders it sufficiently soluble for intravenous injection (for patients who cannot swallow at all).

Nitrogenous fertilisers

Nitrogen uptake by plants is essential for the production of proteins and nucleic acids. Whilst the bulk of the plant is non-nitrogenous cellulose and water, enzymes and co-enzymes (ATP, NADH) are necessary for the metabolic processes of the cell, and RNA and DNA are necessary for control and reproduction.

The nitrogen can only be taken up by green plants (unaided by symbiotic bacteria) as inorganic nitrate, NO_3^-, and fertilisers like potassium nitrate (natural), calcium nitrate and ammonium nitrate (both synthetic) are obviously advantageous to plant growth. Indeed, potassium nitrate contains essential K^+, and ammonium nitrate (Figure 2.7) contains nitrogen in both the cation and the anion.

Forms other than nitrates, e.g. ammonium sulphate, are less efficient. The ammonium ion must be oxidised by soil bacteria. Not only may the ion be washed from the soil by the action of rain, but competitive oxidation to nitrogen may also cause losses. However, the nitrate produced is delivered more slowly. The conversion of organic compounds also involves both hydrolysis and initial reduction to ammonia: this must be even less efficient and slower.

What, then, are the drawbacks of inorganic fertilisers? The two main objections, both of which can be overcome with care, are as follows:

- The nitrogen is delivered in one dose – if too large, it can cause excessive growth, which may encourage foliage rather than flowers and fruit.

- Local concentration of the fertiliser can cause burning and shrivelling.

An objection, not related to crop growth, is that the great solubility of nitrates and ammonium salts can more easily result in 'run-off' during heavy rain and pollution of water-courses. This can lead to excessive plant growth in rivers. When the plants die, the bacterial breakdown lowers the oxygen level of the water, with death of higher forms of aquatic life (eutrophication).

Figure 2.8 Plant growth is affected by amount of fertiliser: too little, just right, or too much?

What ion present in ammonium sulphate causes its aqueous solution to be acidic? Explain your answer.

A particular objection to ammonium nitrate and ammonium sulphate is that, being the salts of a weak base and strong acids, their solutions are acidic.

Plants take up water by osmosis and capillary attraction. The water passes from a low concentration of solutes outside the roots to a higher concentration of solutes in the plant. For those not familiar with osmosis, it sometimes seems more logical to consider the water passing from a high external concentration of water to a lower one inside the plant.

The evolution of plants took place long before the use of artificial fertilisers. The environmental water (essentially rain water) in which they evolved was of a low solute concentration.

The osmotic pressure of an aqueous solution is a measure of its tendency to take up water when separated from water by a membrane through which only this solvent will pass. It is directly proportional to the molar concentration of any solutes, i.e. inversely proportional to their average relative molecular mass. Simple salts increase the osmotic pressure of a solution drastically: if they give rise to two ions per 'molecule', their average relative molecular mass is halved. Plants take up water quite slowly unless deprivation has caused them to droop and increase the concentration of cell fluids: then, when it rains, they may take up water more quickly.

A local concentration of solutes in the environmental water, especially of inorganic salts of low molecular mass, leads to a situation where uptake of water cannot occur or, worse, may even be reversed.

Inorganic fertiliser must be delivered with care. Salts adhering to foliage and wetted by dew or irrigation can 'burn'; their leaves are dehydrated and their cell walls may be ruptured by reversed osmosis. Local lumps of such fertilisers can produce too high a concentration, when dissolved, around roots.

With the exception of urea, H_2NCONH_2, organic fertilisers are of biochemical origin. They vary from expensive dried blood or hoof-and-horn products, from abattoirs, to farmyard manure and slurry (Figure 2.10) and domestic compost heaps. Apart from urea, they have a low nitrogen content, the dried blood being the richest. The combination of high molecular mass and low solubility cannot cause any osmotic problems. Indeed, at certain times of the year, farmers put down huge amounts of material on pastures with no significant detriment to the grass (other than temporary top-growth damage by loss of light).

During the second half of the twentieth century, Israel has developed an extensive agricultural industry. River water, containing minute amounts of naturally dissolved minerals, has been used for irrigation. Recently, in many such areas, crop yields have fallen. Suggest why.

Figure 2.9 A hazard of nitrogenous fertilisers – eutrophication. Algae bloom in a lake polluted by fertiliser, stifling other forms of life

THE COMMERCIAL IMPORTANCE OF ORGANIC COMPOUNDS

Figure 2.10 There may be more nitrogen in the bags than in the 'muck-spreader'

Apart from the low nitrogen content, the disadvantage of such materials is that they must be broken down by bacteria, with loss of some of the nitrogen to the atmosphere. Against this must be set the improvement in the soil by the breakdown of other organic matter, the encouragement of worm activity, and the advantage of a slow and steady release of nitrogen over an extended period.

An intermediate position is taken by urea. This synthetic organic fertiliser is very soluble in water and contains 47% nitrogen, higher than any other fertiliser applicable by normal means. Its molecular mass, 60, is of the same order as the average molecular masses of the ions in inorganic fertilisers ($\frac{1}{2}K^+NO_3^- = 50.5$; $\frac{1}{2}NH_4^+NO_3^- = 40$), and so osmotic effects are similar. But, unlike ammonium nitrate, its aqueous solution is neutral.

Urea has the advantage of other organic fertilisers that it releases its nitrogen slowly by hydrolysis:

$$H_2NCONH_2 \; + \; H_2O \; \rightarrow \; 2NH_3 \; + \; CO_2$$

Its high solubility makes it susceptible to being washed away by rain.

Adhesives

Introduction

Until the present century, industry relied on a handful of adhesives. Bone glue and fish glue were used for woodwork and furniture-making. They were obtained by boiling bones, hooves, skin or fish waste with water, filtering and evaporating the complex mixture of protein and other nitrogenous compounds to a viscous glue or a hard glass. Flour pastes, obtained by heating various cereal flours with water, were colloidal suspensions, mainly of starch, and were used in bookbinding and wallpaper-hanging. Partial hydrolysis of starch, achieved by boiling with acid, gave a sticky mixture of "dextrins", which was used as an adhesive on postage stamps, labels and envelope flaps.

Adhesives generally stick things together by coming into sufficiently close contact with the material to form strong intermolecular attractive forces (van der Waals forces) with the surface. They rarely form any covalent bonds with the material. Two solid surfaces, however well-matched, will never meet with the proximity of particles in a crystal. As van der Waals forces (or even ionic bonds) effectively cease to exist beyond these distances, a liquid has to be applied that wets both surfaces and then solidifies. The strength of the resulting 'join' depends on the strength of the two solids, the strength of the solid adhesive between them, and the strength of the interface forces between the solid and the solid adhesive. If one of the surfaces is not clean, and the adhesive and solid are separated by a layer of dirt one or two molecules thick, then this is the weakest link: the strength of the 'join' is only as strong as the dirt or its attraction for one of the solids on either side. If the solid adhesive is not mechanically strong, then that is the weakest link. If the force of adhesion between the solid and the solid adhesive is not strong, then the situation can

What has recently heightened awareness of the dangers of using untreated abattoir products on agricultural land?

sometimes be improved by roughening the surface (providing a 'key'). The adhesive then flows into irregularities and, after solidifying, it is partly held by the interlocking of the solids (like a dovetail joint or interlocking bricks). If the adhesive is well chosen, e.g. a polymeric polar adhesive to stick to a polar material, then roughening should be of no benefit.

Today, there is a huge number of synthetic adhesives, ranging from instant sticky tape and contact adhesives to partially nitrated carbohydrate wallpaper pastes and superglue. We can only look at one class in detail, the epoxy resins.

Epoxy resins

Epoxy resins are very powerful adhesives. They have been used to stick together a variety of things, from glass handles on glass doors to the parts of light aircraft. Typically, they consist of two parts, resin and hardener.

The resins owe their names to the use of epoxy compounds as a means of polymerisation. They are often made from 3-chloroepoxypropane (epichlorhydrin) and 2,2-di(4-hydroxyphenyl)propane (bisphenol-A), both of which are products of the petrochemical industry (Figure 2.11).

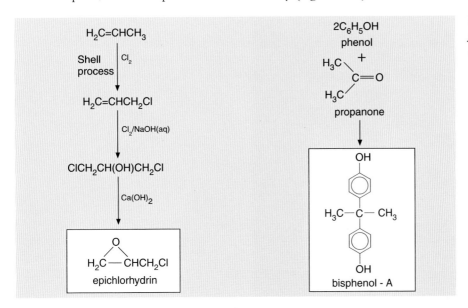

Figure 2.11 Industrial reaction schemes for producing epichlorhydrin and bisphenol-A, and their structures

In the discussion that follows, we shall refer to the two starting materials (for convenience) by their industrial names, and represent the bisphenol-A molecule as HO—☐—OH. Phenols are weakly acidic, and in basic conditions the molecule would form the anions HO—☐—O⁻ and ⁻O—☐—O⁻. These nucleophiles rapidly attack the —CH_2Cl group and displace Cl^- (Figure 2.12). The chain can be extended by attack of unreacted phenol or dimer on the epoxide group (Figure 2.13). An excess of epoxide is always used.

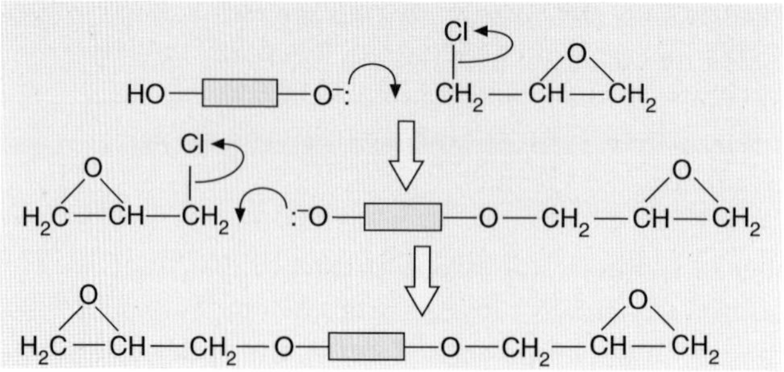

THE COMMERCIAL IMPORTANCE OF ORGANIC COMPOUNDS

Figure 2.12 Formation of shortest chain in epoxy resin

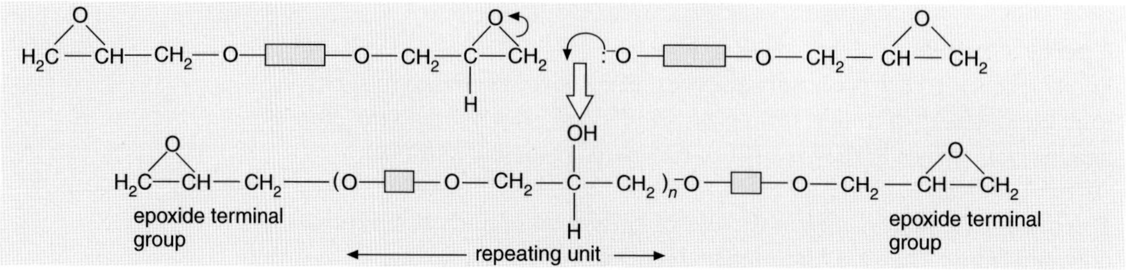

Figure 2.13 Further polymerisation to produce resin

epoxide terminal group

epoxide terminal group

repeating unit

The greater the proportion of epoxide to bisphenol-A, the shorter the chains will be. If the ratio of epoxide to bisphenol-A were 2:1, then, on average, the chains would be limited to the one labelled "shortest chain' in Figure 2.12. In practice, the initial resin has chains with n-values as small as 3 or 4. The larger the value of n, the more viscous is the resin, which will have to be mixed with the hardener at some stage. Provided the epoxide is in excess, the resin molecule will have an epoxy group at each end. We shall represent it by:

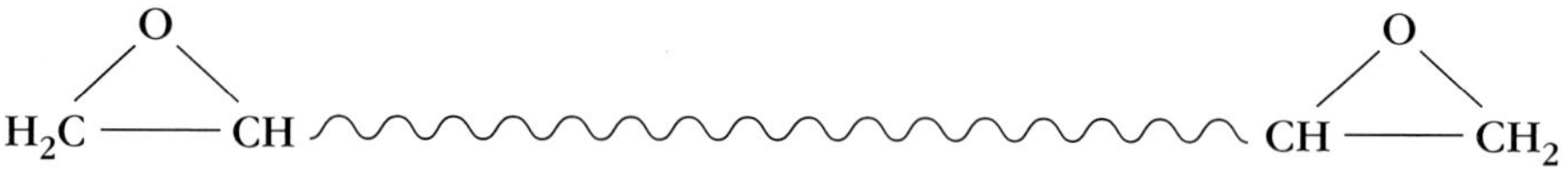

The resin is mixed with a hardener. Traditionally this is a (foul-smelling) polyamine with at least three amino groups per molecule. The amine acts as a nucleophile and attacks the terminal epoxy groups of the resin, joining the molecules in a three-dimensional macrostructure in the hardening and curing stages that follow mixing (Figure 2.14).

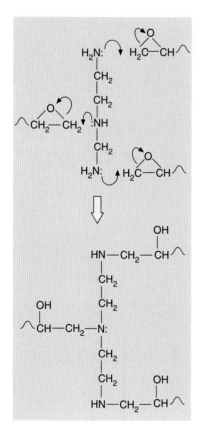

Figure 2.14 Hardening process and formation of cross-linkages

The resulting cross-linked polymer takes from five minutes to an hour to set or harden at room temperature, but goes on curing and gaining mechanical strength for several days. As the resin sets, it becomes more difficult (if not impossible) for the final reactions to occur as free molecular movement is hindered. Thus, in theory, the product (see Figure 2.14) still has two secondary amine groups (—NH—), which could undergo further reaction with terminal epoxies. In reality, the hardening polymer may be too rigid to allow further reaction.

The resulting co-polymer is hard and glass-like. It is strong enough to form bridges across glued surfaces that are ill-matched (unlike, for example, cyanacrylate 'superglues'). It can be coloured and, above all, it can be used to form free-standing laminates and composites. Used with glass-fibre matting, it can be moulded and shaped into strong, light-weight sheets and panels, and is popular in boat-building, etc.

Not all two-component resin–hardener adhesives and fillers are of this type. Many use homolytic co-polymer mechanisms with organic peroxide initiators to harden them.

Addition polymers

Introduction

Fifty years ago, the paper bag was used in shops as virtually the only means of packaging and transport of everything from sweets to vegetables. It didn't stretch (at all) and had relatively low tensile strength. It frequently split and the contents fell out. It adhered to anything mildly sticky and left paper fragments attached to sweets. It lost its strength when wet, and a bag of damp potatoes was a liability! It was not waterproof and meat and fish had to be wrapped several times. But it was biodegradable! If it was not burned on an open fire in the kitchen, it would rot down in the household waste. The plastic bag, usually polythene (the commercial name for poly(ethene)), has changed all that. Unfortunately, it is not biodegradable, but that may be a temporary state of affairs.

Hessian sacks holding potatoes in damp surroundings would rot. Hemp ropes and fishing nets, exposed to rain and sea water, did the same. Wool and cotton motor car carpets used to wear badly: wet shoes and leaking (natural) rubber windscreen surrounds caused carpets to trap water and rot. Non-biodegradable poly(propene) with its great wear-resistance has uses as diverse as sacking, ropes and carpets in hotels, offices, cars and department stores.

Electric cable and 'flex' was covered by rubber and cotton. Rubber perishes and cracks through atmospheric oxidation, and cotton rots in damp places through bacterial and fungal action. This created electrical hazards. PVC has changed all that.

Curved visors for motor cyclists would have been impossible and goggles had glass to protect the eyes. Glass screens on cars were a safety hazard, and on light aircraft and gliders added unnecessary weight. Perspex and polycarbonates have made an enormous contribution here, but glass is cheap, non-flammable and hard enough not to scratch easily. Plastics and glass have achieved a marriage in the laminated windscreen. The outer layers of glass remain unscratched, but the screen will only crack (not shatter!) on impact because the layer of plastic material in between prevents shattering.

The nature of addition polymerisation

Addition polymerisation is energetically favourable (Figure 2.15). Unsaturated monomers are encouraged to form a more stable, singly bonded structure. The value shown in the figure is approximate because the monomer may not be in the gaseous state, the polymer will certainly not be, and the bond enthalpies of C=C and C—C are only approximate and depend on their structural environment. Even reduced to an approximate figure of $-100\,kJ$ per mole of C=C, it represents a considerable increase in thermodynamic stability on polymerisation.

Figure 2.15 Formation of addition polymer from a simple energy viewpoint

The reaction can be visualised as

$$C=C \quad C=C \quad C=C \quad C=C \quad \rightarrow \quad -C-C-C-C-C-C-C-C-$$

All the unmarked bonds 'stay the same'. If n molecules combine, where n is large, and the 'tails' can be ignored, then there is a reduction in energy:

bond energy (enthalpy) of n $C=C$ bonds $= n \times 600$ kJ $= 600n$ kJ

bond energy (enthalpy) of $2n$ $C-C$ bonds $= 2n \times 350$ kJ $= 700n$ kJ

Approximate enthalpy of formation of polymer $= -100n$ kJ

Given the requisite activation energy, it will certainly occur, but the results are less simple than our treatment would suggest. Three related problems arise:

- Is polymerisation ordered or disordered (Figure 2.17a)?

- Is it possible for side-chains to develop (Figure 2.17b)?

- How will the chains pack together (Figure 2.16)?

Figure 2.16 Chains could lie neatly side-by-side, like dry spaghetti before cooking, or form an untidy tangle, like cooked spaghetti

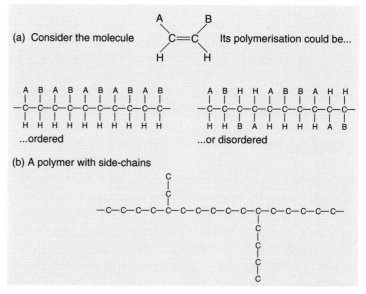

Figure 2.17 Various structures are possible in single polymer molecules

Mechanism of addition polymerisation

Addition polymerisation is essentially a chain reaction. An active molecule, the **initiator**, attacks and joins on to an alkene, creating a larger active molecule. This continues to add on more alkene molecules, the **propagation step**, until a reaction occurs, the **termination** step, in which it loses its high chemical activity. Such polymerisation may be homolytic or heterolytic.

Homolytic polymerisation

The scheme for homolytic polymerisation is shown in Figure 2.18. The initiator is a free radical, R•, e.g. a peroxide. The new radical formed can then react with another alkene molecule, to form a longer radical. Eventually, **termination** of free-radical polymerisation occurs by attack on an established chain. Unfortunately, termination of one chain might very well initiate a reaction in part of an established chain. The new radical then grows 'from the middle'. This tends to produce untidy, branched-chain structures that do not pack well. Since melting point and mechanical strength depend on the force between molecules, and this falls off very rapidly with separation, such branched polymers soften and melt easily and have poor mechanical strength.

Heterolytic (ionic) polymerisation

Heterolytic polymerisation may be cationic or anionic, depending on whether the initiator is an electrophile, resulting in a positively charged (cationic) growing chain, or a nucleophile, resulting in a negatively charged (anionic) growing chain. For alkenes, cationic initiation is to be expected (cf. the action of bromine and lithium aluminium hydride on alkenes and carbonyl compounds). Cationic polymerisation is summarised in Figure 2.19. Cationic polymerisation developed from the discoveries of Ziegler and Natta. Ionic polymerisation tends to give desirable linear polymers since there is negligible tendency for ions to break a covalent C—H bond in an (already formed) alkane chain.

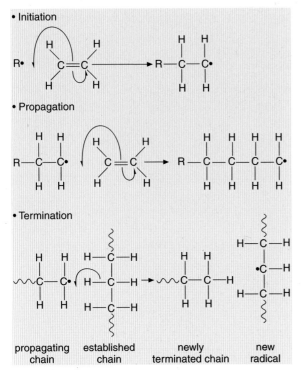

Figure 2.18 The three stages in homolytic polymerisation

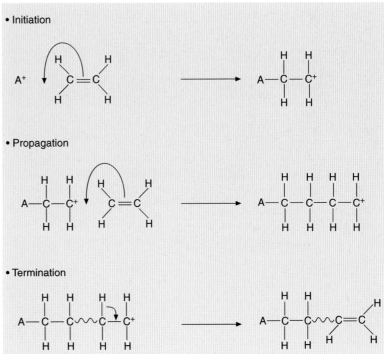

Figure 2.19 The three stages in heterolytic (cationic) polymerisation

Some common polyalkenes

poly(ethene)

Figure 2.20 Using poly(ethene) to protect delicate crops

poly(propene)

Al (C₂H₅)₃
triethyl-aluminium
TiCl₃
titanium(III) chloride

Poly(ethene)

The early commercial poly(ethene) was made by homolytic addition polymerisation. The reaction was initiated by traces of oxygen at high temperature and high pressure. The product was a low-density material (LDPE) with a branched structure and was of limited use. It was mechanically weak: bags burst and kitchenware distorted in the presence of hot or boiling water.

Cationically polymerised poly(ethene) is unbranched, of higher density (HDPE) and higher melting point, and has greater mechanical strength. Whilst there is still limited use for the cheaper LDPE for wrapping and for 'squeezy' dispensers of washing-up liquid, HDPE has completely replaced it for kitchenware (Figure 2.20).

Poly(propene)

Early attempts to produce poly(propene) by a homolytic route gave a completely useless product. It is now a substance of enormous commercial importance, and is made by cationic polymerisation of propene at slightly elevated temperatures and pressures using a Ziegler–Natta catalyst. One of the first such catalysts was a coordination complex of triethyl-aluminium and titanium(III) chloride. The complex forms a larger complex with the propene molecule and the chain grows from this active centre. Once the geometry of the initial complex is established, any one chain grows with retention of that geometry. The resulting poly(propene) has a zig-zag backbone with all the side-chain methyl groups on one side, either above or below the plane of the zig-zag (but not both), as shown in Figure 2.21.

Such a structure is said to be **stereoregular**, and, in particular, this stereoregular structure is classed as **isotactic**. It packs well in the solid state. The resulting poly(propene) is of relatively high density, and has a high melting point, high tensile strength and good resistance to wear. It is widely used for ropes and sacking and for carpets and carpet tiles (Figure 2.22). Domestic carpets tend to be blended with wool; those for hotels and offices, where wear is considerable, are blended with synthetic fibres. Its very low electrical conductivity gives it a tendency to become charged by friction, especially in dry centrally heated environments. People have often experienced mild electric shocks after walking on it and stepping into lifts or touching metal objects. Surface treatment of the fibres and blending can help to reduce this.

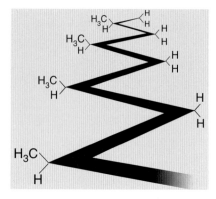

Figure 2.21 The zig-zag structure of isotactic poly(propene)

Figure 2.22 Poly(propene) has high tensile strength and resists wear well – essential in fishing nets

Poly(chloroethene)

This polymer (also known as PVC) is widely used as an electrical insulator, as a cheap leather substitute for handbags and furniture, and for the manufacture of floor coverings (Figure 2.23). Rigidity and weather resistance have allowed its extensive use for guttering, drain-pipes and window frames.

When used for waterproof clothing, it is used in sheet form not as fibres (because of its lack of tensile strength). Here, and in its use for covering car seats, its hydrophobic nature makes it feel uncomfortable in hot weather when perspiration is trapped. The widely differing properties required of a rigid hard-wearing floor tile and a soft seat covering are achieved by using hard-wearing mineral fillers or organic plasticisers in the polymer.

Poly(tetrafluoroethene)

The extremely stable C—F bond makes this polymer very resistant to chemical attack. It has a low coefficient of friction, which makes it very slippery. It is thus suitable for the moving parts of taps that are difficult to lubricate and in contact with chemicals, e.g. burette taps. A thin PTFE tape is widely used by plumbers to wrap around the screw threads of pipe joints (Figure 2.24): it seals the gaps between the screw threads without making the joint impossible to unscrew – indeed its lubricating properties have the opposite effect. It is also used in 'non-stick' coatings.

Its manufacture involves the use of fluorine, an element both hazardous to obtain and to handle. It is thus a relatively expensive polymer.

Polystyrene

This polymer, the recommended systematic name of which is poly(phenylethene), is commonly used in two forms. A hard, high-density form is often seen as the transparent yellow handles of screwdrivers, and a low-density expanded form is familiar as an unbelievably light packing material (Figure 2.25).

The advantage of the latter form stems from its ability to be expanded by gas bubbles to many times its original (true) volume and, at the same time, to be moulded into the shapes of the items it is intended to protect. The packing material hardly increases the weight, and therefore the cost of transport, but it combines crushability and rigidity in such a way as to be damaged sacrificially by impact. It is also packed around objects for transport in the form of pellets.

poly(chloroethene)
(PVC)

Figure 2.23 Rigidity and resistance to wear make poly(chloroethene) an excellent choice for pipes

poly(tetrafluoroethene)
(PTFE, teflon)

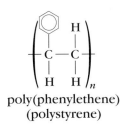

poly(phenylethene)
(polystyrene)

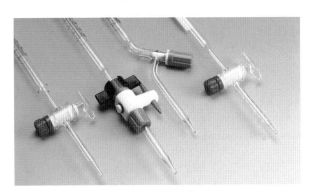

Figure 2.24 Poly(tetrafluoroethene), or PTFE, resists chemical attack well. The taps on these burettes are made from it

Figure 2.25 Low density polystyrene floats well in water

The inclusion of air or gas bubbles in the structure also makes it an excellent thermal insulator. It is used for ceiling tiles, the interior of refrigerator doors and casings and between partition walls of houses. Unfortunately, it is highly flammable, but its ease of ignition may be partially reduced by the addition of non-flammable matter during the expansion process.

Condensation polymers

Introduction

Condensation polymers are those which appear to have been formed by the elimination of water or some other simple substance, such as ammonia or hydrogen chloride, between successive monomers (Figure 2.26).

Figure 2.26 Formation of polyesters, polyamides and polyethers by condensation

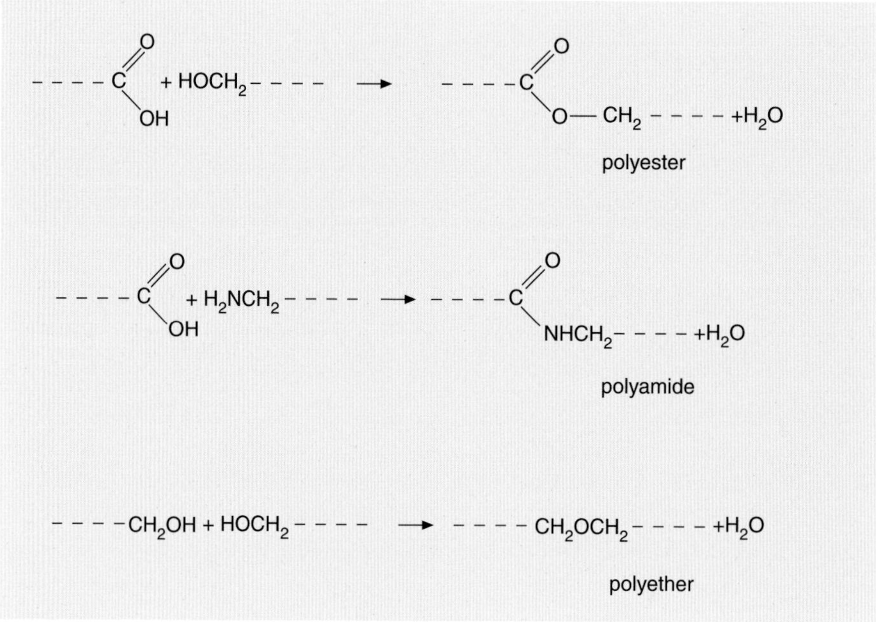

In the simplest cases the monomers are bifunctional and produce linear molecules. The materials are usually of high tensile strength and make good fibres. Because the reactions by which they are formed are usually reversible, however, unlike the polyalkenes, which have continuous carbon chains, they are often not resistant to chemical attack.

Nylons

These polyamides can be made by polymerisation or co-polymerisation depending on whether one monomer (with both an amino and a carboxyl group) or two monomers (each with two amino or two carboxyl groups) are used. Thus co-polymerisation of 1,6-diaminohexane and hexane-1,6-dioic acid (adipic acid) gives nylon-6,6 (the numbers reflect the numbers of carbon atoms in the amine and acid molecules):

$$n\text{H}_2\text{N}(\text{CH}_2)_6\text{NH}_2 \quad + \quad n\text{HO}_2\text{C}(\text{CH}_2)_4\text{CO}_2\text{H}$$

$$\rightarrow \quad \text{H}[\text{NH}(\text{CH}_2)_6\text{NHCO}(\text{CH}_2)_4\text{CO}]_n\text{OH} \quad + \quad (2n-1)\text{H}_2\text{O}$$

nylon-6,6

One of the most widely used nylons is nylon-6 (i.e. one monomer with six carbon atoms per molecule). This is obtained, in theory, by polycondensation of an amino acid with H_2N— at one end of the molecule and —CO_2H at the other. In practice, it is obtained from the cyclic amide, caprolactam, by rearrangement (ring opening) and polyaddition:

$$\underset{\text{caprolactam}}{\begin{array}{c} CH_2-CH_2 \\ H_2C \qquad\qquad C=O \\ \qquad\qquad NH \\ CH_2-CH_2 \end{array}} \quad \xrightarrow[\text{heat}]{} \quad \underset{\text{nylon - 6}}{-(\,HN(CH_2)_5CO\,)_n}$$

Nylons are widely used for fibres. They may be used as monofilament (extruded and stretched but unspun) for fishing lines, strimmer cords and toothbrush bristles, or they may be spun into yarn, perhaps with threads of a natural fibres (Figure 2.27). The natural fibres trap air better, and the garments feel warmer: they are also more moisture-absorbent and feel less 'clammy'. The harder, more wear-resistant nylon gives durability.

Figure 2.27 Some nylon products

The slippery nature of solid nylon has led to its extensive use for plain bearings on small carts, lawn-mower wheels and children's toys, etc., and for gear wheels in light machinery, e.g. clocks (Figure 2.27).

Polyesters

Polyesters are typified by terylene, the co-polymer of terephthalic acid (benzene-1,4-dicarboxylic acid) and ethylene glycol (ethane-1,2-diol):

$$n HO_2CC_6H_4CO_2H \quad + \quad n HOCH_2CH_2OH$$
$$\rightarrow \quad HO(OCC_6H_4COOCH_2CH_2O)_nH \quad + \quad (n-1)H_2O$$

These polymers are similar to nylon but have superior strength as fibres.

Biodegradability and polymers

The disposal of waste synthetic polymers, particularly those used as packaging material, has caused much environmental concern. Ideally, recycling would make use of what are, in effect, products of the limited resources of the Earth's petroleum. In practice, the time and the workforce required for collecting and sorting plastic materials, and the cost of cleaning and recycling them, are normally very uneconomic when compared with the cost of new polymers.

The problem would be lessened, at least for the present generation, if the polymers could be made biodegradable. Natural polymers such as wool and silk (which are proteins – co-polymers of many amino acids) or wood and cotton and hence paper (polymers of glucose) are sometimes inconveniently biodegradable. Indeed, industry spends millions of pounds a year on chemicals to protect carpets from insect damage and wood from fungal action. One approach that has proved successful in making synthetic polymers biodegradable is to incorporate repeated biodegradable links, e.g. a few glucose units between short lengths of the polymer chain. The material can then be broken down, at these 'recognisable' links, into submicroscopic non-biodegradable particles by fungal or bacterial action. This alteration of structure is not easy and increases the cost of the material. Furthermore, it must be done without significantly reducing the essential mechanical properties of the polymer.

The internal combustion engine and its fuels

Introduction

The majority of conventional internal combustion engines have four 'strokes'. A piston reciprocates (goes up and down) in a cylinder fitted with an inlet valve (or valves), to control the inlet of fuel and air, and an outlet valve, to allow the expulsion of combustion products (Figure 2.28).

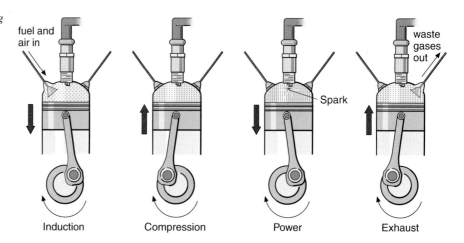

Figure 2.28 A simplified diagram showing the principles of the four-stroke cycle

Induction of fuel and air through the open inlet valve is followed by **compression** of the mixture. At a critical point in the four-stroke cycle, at about the time of greatest compression, a spark produced at a spark-plug ignites the mixture in the cylinder and a wave of flame spreads through it:

$$C_8H_{18}(g) \quad + \quad 12\tfrac{1}{2}O_2(g) \quad \rightarrow \quad 8CO_2(g) \quad + \quad 9H_2O(g)$$

The enormous pressure of the hot combustion products (and nitrogen) forces down the piston in the **power** stroke. The rising piston then expels the gases through the exhaust.

Pre-ignition and related problems

In theory, the more the mixture of fuel and air can be compressed, the more power will be developed by the engine. Unfortunately, the rapid act of (adiabatic) compression, in a cylinder already hot, raises the temperature of the mixture to such an extent that pre-ignition may occur. The fuel–air mixture detonates (starting simultaneously at many points) before the spark appears. Instead of a smooth flame of combustion spreading outwards from the spark, building up pressure over a period of the order of a millisecond, an 'instant' explosion subjects the engine to severe shock. This 'knocking' or 'pinking' causes loss of power and damage to the engine.

CH₃ ... (structure)

$$\begin{array}{ccc} & CH_3 & CH_3 \\ & | & | \\ H_3C - C - CH_2 - CH - CH_3 \\ & | \\ & CH_3 \end{array}$$

2,2,4-trimethylpentane
('iso octane')

Chemists soon discovered that the less-branched ('straighter') alkanes show a greater tendency to pre-ignite. Fuels were given an octane number to put them on a quality scale between the worst imaginable fuel, heptane ($CH_3CH_2CH_2CH_2CH_2CH_2CH_3$, an unbranched alkane), with an 'octane number' of 0, and 2,2,4-trimethylpentane, with an 'octane number' of 100. The branched alkane 2,2,4-trimethylpentane is an isomer of octane, hence the name of the scale.

Pre-ignition is radical-induced, and species that can combine with radicals can be used to inhibit it. Tetraethyl-lead, $Pb(C_2H_5)_4$, was increasingly added to fuels as more and more powerful engines were developed. In the 1960s and 1970s, filling stations sold heavily leaded petrol with octane ratings above 100, later classed as 'five star'. The lead(II) oxide, produced as the fuel burned, tended to cover the piston crown, cylinder head, plugs and valves with a hard coating, and this was prevented, as far as possible, by adding 1,2-dibromoethane, so that the lead could be expelled harmlessly(!) into the atmosphere as the relatively volatile lead(II) bromide.

Internal combustion engines and the environment

The exhaust gases from a petrol engine, in addition to water vapour, are likely to give rise to some or all of the following pollution problems:

- The unavoidable expulsion of carbon dioxide is believed to be contributing to global warming by enhancing the 'greenhouse effect' of the natural carbon dioxide.

- Carbon monoxide is a well known poison which, with haemoglobin in blood, reversibly forms carboxyhaemoglobin. This compound is more stable than the oxyhaemoglobin formed between haemoglobin and molecular oxygen. Short-term contact with carbon monoxide can lead to unconsciousness and death, but the gas is known to have chronic effects in those subject to small amounts over long periods, e.g. traffic police.

- The oxides of nitrogen, apart from causing acid rain, are a serious health risk, especially to those with breathing problems.

- Long-term statistical studies suggest that ingestion of lead compounds impedes brain development in the young.

- Unburnt or partially burnt hydrocarbons can be carcinogenic. They react with oxides of nitrogen in sunlight to give 'photochemical smog' (Figure 2.29), and if they reach the upper atmosphere they will destroy ozone.

Figure 2.29 Photochemical smog

These pollutants arise from two causes. Some are the inevitable result of burning hydrocarbons in the conditions of an internal combustion (IC) engine, and some are the result of measures taken to prevent pre-ignition. We shall look at them in that order.

Pollution due to burning hydrocarbons

A mixture of a gaseous hydrocarbon fuel and oxygen must burn very quickly if it is to drive an IC engine efficiently. Ideally, the air should be in excess, a 'weak' mixture, so that only carbon dioxide and water are formed. If the mixture is too weak, misfiring and inefficient combustion may occur, leading to the expulsion of partially burnt fuel. If the mixture is 'rich', i.e. the ratio of air to fuel is less than the stoichiometric ratio, then carbon monoxide must be formed and some fuel may be unburnt.

Until recently, carburettors were used to mix fuel and air. These sprayed droplets of fuel into the air stream and, because of their inability to cope perfectly with the varying requirements of the engine, they erred on the rich side to avoid misfiring. As a result, the car engine emitted an unacceptably high amount of carbon monoxide. Carburettors are small, relatively cheap devices, and they are still used on small engines, e.g. for lawn-mowers.

When the mixture is rich, there is little tendency to form oxides of nitrogen. Nitrogen is unreactive and, despite its presence in huge excess, it is unable to compete with easily oxidised carbon monoxide or hydrocarbons for a limited supply of oxygen. The reversible formation of nitrogen oxide (nitrogen monoxide) is endothermic:

$$N_2(g) \quad + \quad O_2(g) \quad \rightleftharpoons \quad 2NO(g); \qquad \Delta H \quad = \quad +180 \, kJ \, mol^{-1}$$

and its formation is thus favoured at high temperatures.

The flame of the burning fuel is hottest if the stoichiometric ratio is achieved, and thus the amount of nitrogen oxide in the exhaust reaches a maximum for a slightly weak mixture, i.e. one with oxygen 'to spare'. Nitrogen oxide is oxidised in the atmosphere as it cools because the oxidation is exothermic:

$$2NO(g) \quad + \quad O_2(g) \quad \rightleftharpoons \quad 2NO_2(g); \qquad \Delta H \quad = -110 \, kJ \, mol^{-1}$$

THE COMMERCIAL IMPORTANCE OF ORGANIC COMPOUNDS

The atmospheric mixture of oxides of nitrogen is often given the formula NO_x. It is thus very difficult to minimise the formation of CO without encouraging the formation of NO_x. Figure 2.30 shows how the exhaust gas composition changes as the air:fuel ratio is increased.

Pollution due to preventing pre-ignition

The addition of lead compounds to reduce pre-ignition is environmentally unacceptable and is being phased out. The alternatives are to add more highly branched alkanes or to add aromatic compounds such as benzene (which is the cheaper solution). Unfortunately, aromatic compounds are very stable and are often carcinogenic. Benzene vapour escapes from the vehicle tank when filling it with fuel. Aromatic compounds tend to form traces of polynuclear hydrocarbons during incomplete combustion and these are invariably carcinogenic.

Minimising the problems of pollution

Fuel injection can control the air:fuel ratio far better than carburettors and is gradually replacing them. Gas analysis probes in the exhaust system can instantly send back information about the presence (weak mixture) or absence (rich mixture) of oxygen. Electronically controlled injection systems can respond 'instantly' by correcting the air:fuel ratio.

The reduction in the lead content of fuel and hence of exhaust gases allowed the use of catalytic converters. Coupled with the tight mixture control afforded by fuel injection, excellent emission control can be achieved. The majority of catalytic converters fitted to cars use systems of two catalysts. One, typically rhodium, decomposes the oxides of nitrogen at the lower, more favourable temperature of the exhaust pipe:

$$2NO(g) \ \rightleftharpoons \ N_2(g) \ + \ O_2(g)$$

The other catalyst, typically platinum, oxidises carbon monoxide and unburnt hydrocarbons (with the oxygen produced):

$$2CO(g) \ + \ O_2(g) \ \rightleftharpoons \ 2CO_2(g)$$

Diesel engines

Diesel engines employ a four-stroke cycle like petrol engines. The main differences are that the much less volatile diesel fuel is injected near the end of the compression stroke into the very hot air. The extent of compression (compression ratio) is much higher than in petrol engines, and the fuel–air mixture is deliberately detonated: there is no conventional spark-plug. They make more efficient use of their fuel.

The engines need to be much stronger and are thus heavier and more expensive: lubricating oils need to pass more stringent tests. The constant explosive ignition produces a typical diesel rattle, which designers try to conceal.

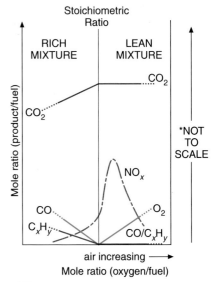

(* NO_x **greatly** exaggerated)

Figure 2.30 The change in composition of the exhaust gas as the air:fuel ratio increases

THE COMMERCIAL IMPORTANCE OF ORGANIC COMPOUNDS

Figure 2.31 Badly regulated emission from a diesel engine

The principal disadvantage of the diesel engine is the so-called 'particulate emission' (Figure 2.31). You will be familiar with the smoke and soot produced when higher hydrocarbons are burned. This is minimised in all internal combustion engines by mixing the fuel vapour and air efficiently. However, the higher molecular mass of diesel fuel results in the inevitable emission of tiny particles of carbon (not soot or smoke – that is just the characteristic of a badly maintained engine). The particles contain carcinogenic residues from the partly combusted fuel and are a very serious environmental problem.

Transport of the rather high-boiling fuel in road tankers presents a much reduced fire hazard, as does a split diesel fuel tank in a road accident.

Solid and gaseous fuels

Solid fuel effectively left the transport scene with the departure of the last steam train. A solid fuel is usually not so easy to ignite as liquid fuels and cannot leak, so is much safer than liquid fuels. However, because it can neither flow through fine pipes and jets, nor vaporise and mix perfectly with air, it is suitable only for external combustion engines. These produce steam by heating water in a pipe or boiler: the steam then drives the piston or turbine. This is thermally inefficient, and the massive engines required are only suitable for large installations like power-stations.

The densities, in liquid form, of hydrogen, methane and octane are 0.070, 0.424 and 0.703 g cm^{-3}, respectively. Which gives out most heat, on combustion, per unit volume?

Gases mix perfectly with air at all temperatures and do not suffer from vaporising problems in cold weather like petrol, diesel or aviation fuel. They are ideal for internal combustion. The combustion of hydrogen yields much more energy, per gram, than that of any saturated hydrocarbon (Table 2.1). The lower, gaseous hydrocarbons, with a higher percentage of hydrogen, yield more energy *per gram* than the higher liquid fuels. This 'weight advantage' of the lower hydrocarbons, however, is largely cancelled out by a 'bulk disadvantage' when they are liquefied: they have lower densities and the energy yield per cubic centimetre tends to even out.

Table 2.1 *Heats of combustion of some fuels*

Fuel	$-\Delta H_c$/kJ mol^{-1}	M_r	Heat of combustion/kJ g^{-1}
Hydrogen (gas)	286	2	143
Methane (gas)	890	16	56
Octane (petrol)	5512	114	48

Unfortunately, at low pressure, gases take up a large amount of space; and at high pressure, not only do they constitute a danger through leakage, but they require very heavy containers, which are undesirable in moving vehicles. Nevertheless, experimental public transport systems have been developed in some countries using low-pressure gaseous fuels.

Hazards in organic chemistry

Introduction

Fortunately, the majority of organic compounds are not corrosive, but they are associated with two very general hazards, toxicity and flammability (Figures 2.32 and 2.33). The most important first line of defence against such hazards is in the packaging and labelling of organic chemicals.

Figure 2.32 *Victims of poisoning by industrial leakage of organic compounds*

Figure 2.33 *A fire at an organic chemical works in Thailand*

Packaging

Organic compounds do not normally react with glass. The use of glass containers for small quantities (up to about 2 kg) of material is thus satisfactory. Such containers, however, are frequently doubly packaged for transport, e.g. packed into protective outer cases or drums. Glass bottles containing liquids may also be polythene-coated to prevent leakage if the glass is cracked. Where particularly dangerous materials such as poisonous liquids are involved, the space between the glass container and outer package is often filled with an absorbent material such as chalk or powdered clay. More volatile materials, e.g. ethylamine, are often supplied in small sealed glass ampoules, which must be broken in order to use the contents.

Labelling

Labelling must comply with mandatory standards that apply throughout the EEC and for many other parts of the world. Packages must be clearly labelled: where a bottle is inside a protective container, both must be labelled. The labelling must contain information about the identity of the contents, the potential hazards and the name of the manufacturer, shipper or supplier.

Flammability

Organic compounds are rich in C—H and C—C bonds and are converted to carbon dioxide and water with the evolution of much heat: a fire once started may be difficult to control. The ease of ignition depends mainly on the volatility of the compound, since the vapour must be mixed with air to form the requisite flammable mixture. Thus solids *tend to* offer the lowest risk and gases the highest, and the flammability of a liquid *tends* to decrease with increasing boiling point. Once ignited, if the material is a liquid, it tends to flow uncontrollably; if it is a solid, it melts and does the same. As far as laboratory chemicals are concerned, little can be done to reduce their flammability, since purity and the addition of other materials are contradictory needs. The main use of additives to reduce fire hazard has been in the addition of flame-retardants to polystyrene for house insulation and ceiling tiles, and in foam for furniture manufacture. These raise the ignition temperature and extinguish the fire if the temperature is not too high.

In handling flammable materials in the laboratory, good ventilation is essential to carry away flammable vapours while their concentration is too low to ignite. No-one would dream of heating an open beaker of petrol with a Bunsen burner! But, increasingly, *all* heating operations in organic chemistry, whether of open or closed nature (e.g. boiling under reflux), are carried out electrically with heating mantles (see Figure 3.7) or hot-plates. Hidden sources of flames or sparks must also be avoided: brushless electric motors, which do not produce sparks between moving parts, must be used.

The correct method of disposal of flammable solvents is very important. They must not be put down the sink if they are immiscible with water! Preferably, they should be redistilled and recovered. Liquids that are miscible with water and are not worth recovery, e.g. small amounts of impure lower alcohols, can be safely disposed of down the sink provided that they are accompanied by enough water to make them no longer hazardous. The more water is present, the lower is their vapour pressure (see Chapter 5), and a point is reached at which the vapour cannot form a flammable mixture with air. If the liquid is not miscible with water, however, its vapour pressure is not affected by water in the drains (see steam distillation, Chapter 3). Liquids such as ether or petrol give off high concentrations of vapour. This vapour, always more dense than air, can flow along pipes and perhaps escape into sinks on a lower floor, creating a fire hazard in a different room. It will certainly create a fire or explosion hazard in the sewers. Such liquids should normally be disposed of by controlled incineration.

Laboratory gases are a special hazard. As far as flammability is concerned, hydrogen is the most dangerous, for three reasons:

- It is stored in heavy cylinders (which are themselves a hazard) under very high pressure, e.g. 150 atm (15 MPa). This is because it does not liquefy under pressure at room temperature. It is thus more likely to leak than gases like propane or butane that liquefy at modest pressures.

- The rates of effusion (leakage) of two gases through the same 'pin-hole' at the same temperature and pressure are inversely proportional to (the square roots of) their relative molecular masses. From this, it can be seen that, since hydrogen has the lowest molecular mass of all gases, it must have the highest comparable rate of leakage.

- It is odourless and colourless, and a leak is unobservable.

Whilst hydrogen is not organic, it is widely used in organic chemistry. The cylinders should be stored outside buildings when not in use and should be checked for leaks (with soapy water) at joints in the pipework before use.

Toxicity

Nothing can be done to reduce the toxicity of a material other than by changing its identity or by massive dilution: only the latter is (sometimes) applicable to cleaning up after accidents.

Labelling has already been stated to be the first line of defence. This is equally important when making a compound in a laboratory: a paper label with the name of the compound and your name is a minimal requirement for a beaker, flask or other working apparatus.

Care in handling toxic substances is largely common sense. Good ventilation is required and, if necessary, use a fume cupboard for volatile liquids and gases.

Some materials, like phenol, nitrobenzene or phenylamine, are 'skin poisons': they dissolve in, the surface moisture of the skin, and pass through it. Wearing impervious gloves and washing hands after use are obvious but important precautions.

Figure 2.34 Foam at a weir

Lack of biodegradability

After World War II, the public made a rapid change from 'natural' soap to synthetic detergents for washing clothes. Later, when liquid detergents became available, they were used for manual dish-washing and shampoos. This resulted in a hitherto unknown and unexpected problem (Figure 2.34).

Soaps had always been made by the alkaline hydrolysis of fats and oils (*Principles of Physical and Organic Chemistry*, p.99). This produced soaps that were recognised by bacteria in sewage, sewage treatment plants and rivers. All that had been done in the soap-making process was to break a propane-1,2,3-triol (glycerol) molecule from the fat and replace it by an ionic link to a sodium ion. Soap entering the sewage system was broken down in a few hours in the same way as fatty materials, e.g. waste food particles. The synthetic sodium alkylsulphonates first used by the general public as synthetic soapless detergents were not recognised by bacteria, and passed through sewage plants to produce havoc on river systems at weirs and waterfalls. The problem was overcome by modifying the structures of the hydrocarbon molecules from which the sulphonic acids were made so that they were biodegradable.

Plastics such as poly(ethene), poly(propene) and PVC are not biodegradable. Thoughtless disposal of items made from such materials causes 'permanent' litter. This is not only unsightly but poses dangers to wild-life. Many uses of these materials depend on their non-biodegradability, e.g. poly(propene) sacks and nylon monofilament fishing gear. It is thus important that they are disposed of correctly and either incinerated or recycled.

What special advantage do soapless detergents have over soap?

3 Organic synthesis

You can make anything from anything

From the point of view of the organic chemist, this is probably true, but it would be a foolhardy chemist who tried to make gold from hydrogen. The latter change might be feasible in a supernova, but it certainly is *not* a sound proposition in a chemistry laboratory. Even for the organic chemist, the starting point is never just 'any old thing': it is carefully chosen.

Choice of starting material and route

In reality, the organic chemist tries to make the target compound from the nearest structure that is commercially available. This is often a natural product, e.g. the manufacture of codeine from morphine (page 28).

The route chosen is normally the shortest possible. Organic reactions never give 100% yields. If, on average, each stage of a reaction sequence gave a 50% yield (which would be by no means untypical) and ten stages were required, the final yield would be $(\frac{1}{2})^{10}$, i.e. 1/1024 or 0.1%, of the theoretical: grams from kilograms! A five-stage process, perhaps using more expensive reagents (e.g. lithium aluminium hydride), on the same 50% yield basis, would give $(\frac{1}{2})^5$, or about 30 times as much as the ten-stage alternative.

Compare two possible routes from propanol to butanol. It is very likely that any pathway would begin by preparing bromopropane:

$$C_3H_7OH + KBr + H_2SO_4 \rightarrow C_3H_7Br + KHSO_4 + H_2O$$

Two alternatives (at least) are then possible:

- Route A

$$C_3H_7Br \xrightarrow{\text{step 1}} C_3H_7CN \xrightarrow{\text{step 2}} C_3H_7CH_2NH_2 \xrightarrow{\text{step 3}} C_4H_9OH$$

Step 1: alcoholic potassium or sodium cyanide gives a good yield, but the highly toxic reagent is an obvious hazard.

Step 2: lithium aluminium hydride again gives a good yield but is a very expensive reagent.

Step 3: sodium nitrite and hydrochloric acid gives a very poor yield of butanol.

• Route B

$$\underset{\text{step 1}}{\text{C}_3\text{H}_7\text{Br}} \;\rightarrow\; \underset{\text{step 2}}{\text{C}_3\text{H}_7\text{MgBr}} \;\rightarrow\; \text{C}_4\text{H}_9\text{OH}$$

Step 1: magnesium and ether (solvent) gives an excellent yield of the Grignard reagent, which is used *in situ*.

Step 2: treatment with methanal followed, in situ, by decomposition with aqueous acid gives a good yield of the product.

Route A uses an unpleasant reagent and an expensive reagent, involves three steps and gives a poor yield. Route B is, effectively, one step because the whole sequence is carried out without isolating an intermediate, and it gives a good yield. Route B would be the obvious choice.

Old A-Level papers are full of questions that ask the candidate to make **B** from **A** *without the use of any other organic compounds* (except perhaps solvents), e.g. ethyl ethanoate from ethanol:

$$\text{CH}_3\text{CH}_2\text{OH} \;\underset{}{\overset{\text{K}_2\text{Cr}_2\text{O}_7/\text{H}^+}{\rightleftharpoons}}\; \text{CH}_3\text{CO}_2\text{H} \;\underset{\text{conc H}_2\text{SO}_4}{\overset{\text{ethanol}}{\rightleftharpoons}}\; \text{CH}_3\text{CO}_2\text{CH}_2\text{CH}_3$$

The restriction, here, is to make sure that the candidate does not start by using ethanoic acid but must make it first.

The organic chemist is not fettered by the pedantic demands of the examiner. The best way is the fastest, or the most high yielding or the cheapest.

The inclusion of Grignard reagents in the A-Level syllabus means that there is more opportunity to ask questions in which more than one organic material may be required at some stage. For example, how would you convert propan-2-ol into 2-methylpropan-2-ol? A possible answer is shown in Figure 3.1. Here a Grignard reagent is involved, and it would be rather silly to expect anyone to make it from the propan-2-ol.

**What products would be formed if you used:
(i) butan-2-ol at the start instead of propan-2-ol;
(ii) ethylmagnesium bromide as the Grignard reagent; and (iii) both of these?**

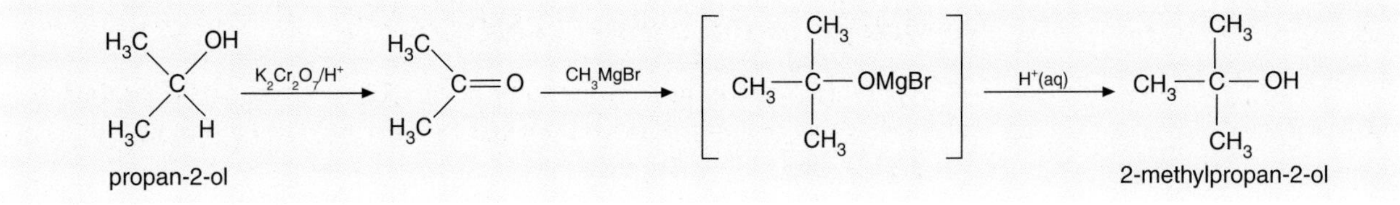

propan-2-ol → (with $\text{K}_2\text{Cr}_2\text{O}_7/\text{H}^+$) → (with CH_3MgBr) → (with $\text{H}^+\text{(aq)}$) → 2-methylpropan-2-ol

Figure 3.1 Reaction scheme to convert propan-2-ol into 2-methylpropan-2-ol

But, even in questions involving Grignard reagents, the old restriction could still be applied. For example, how would you make hexan-3-ol from propan-1-ol using no other organic reagents except solvents. A possible answer is shown in Figure 3.2.

Figure 3.2 Reaction scheme to convert propan-1-ol into hexan-3-ol

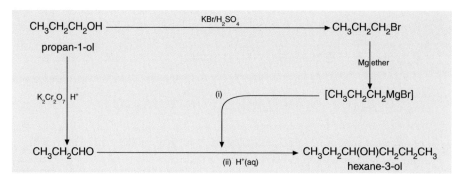

It is important to realise that the organic reactions in the A-Level syllabus are, with the exception of the use of lithium aluminium hydride, all (fairly unsophisticated) nineteenth-century methods. They represent an infinitesimally small fraction of all reactions in use today. Nevertheless, their use illustrates many general principles, e.g. the idea that a group that appears to need retaining may first have to be destroyed and then later replaced. This is the case in the two examples involving Grignard reagents in Figures 3.1 and 3.2, and for the —OH group in the preparation of 2-hydroxy-2-methylpropanenitrile (**B**) from propan-2-ol (**A**) in Figure 3.3. The inexperienced student is likely to look for a way of directly replacing the 2° hydrogen by a cyanide when faced with this problem.

*Figure 3.3 Reaction scheme to convert propan-2-ol (**A**) into 2-hydroxy-2-methylpropanenitrile (**B**)*

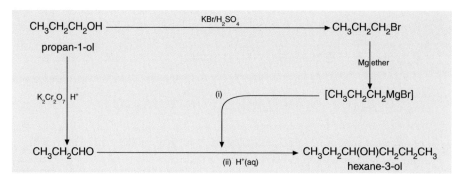

Main groups of synthetic reactions

Synthetic procedures fall roughly into four groups, depending on whether the number of carbon atoms in the carbon skeleton of the molecule is changed. One of the first decisions that must be taken when planning a route is whether such a change is required. The reference to the carbon *skeleton* is necessary because reactions like esterification or ester hydrolysis, whilst changing the number of carbon atoms in the molecule, do not change the size of the carbon skeleton.

No change in the carbon skeleton

Reactions of this type include:

- simple substitution reactions between non-carbon-containing groups, e.g. —OH, —Br, —I, —NH$_2$, etc.

- limited oxidation of alcohols and aldehydes or reduction of aldehydes, ketones, nitriles and acids

- eliminations yielding C═C double bonds, amides and nitriles, ester hydrolysis and esterification

These reactions are usually a necessary preliminary in order to reach a point where the number of carbon atoms can be changed. Some of the more common situations are illustrated in Figure 3.4.

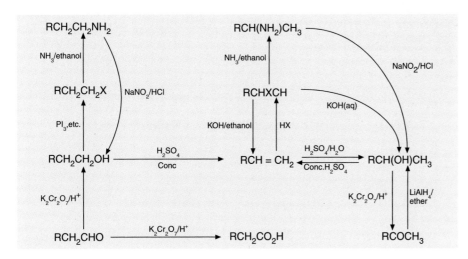

Figure 3.4 Some reactions where there is no change in the carbon skeleton

Number of carbon atoms in the skeleton is increased …

… by one

Such reactions include:

- introduction of the cyanide group by nucleophilic substitution of a haloalkane, or addition of HCN to a carbonyl compound

- introduction of the primary alcohol —CH_2OH or carboxylic acid groups by addition of methanal, HCHO, or carbon dioxide to a Grignard reagent

… by more than one

Such reactions include:

- addition of Grignard reagents to aldehydes and ketones

- Friedel–Crafts additions to aromatic systems

Some of these reactions are shown in Figure 3.5.

Give as many synthetic reactions as you can where there is no change in the carbon skeleton. Then look at Figure 3.4.

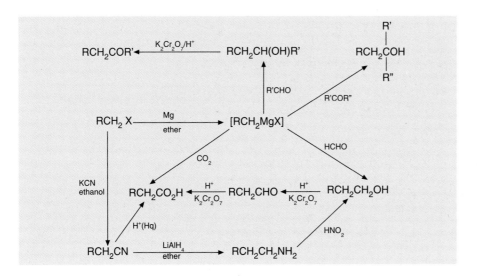

Figure 3.5 Some reactions where there is an increase in the number of carbon atoms in the skeleton

Which important synthetic reaction from the list is missing from Figure 3.5?

Number of carbon atoms in the skeleton is decreased by one (degradations)

These methods include:

- the Hofmann degradation of amides with sodium hydroxide and bromine

$$RCONH_2 \ + \ NaOBr \ \rightarrow \ RNH_2 \ + \ NaBr \ + \ CO_2$$

- the oxidation of aromatic side-chains with potassium manganate(VII)

$$C_6H_5CH_3 \ \xrightarrow{\ KMnO_4/H^+\ } \ C_6H_5CO_2H$$

- the haloform reaction, applied to methyl ketones and methyl secondary alcohols

$$RCH(OH)CH_3 \ \xrightarrow{\ NaOX\ } \ RCOCH_3 \ \xrightarrow{\ NaOX\ } \ RCO_2H$$

where X is a halogen; this is iodine if the reaction is to be used as a test of the presence of the CH_3CO— or $CH_3CH(OH)$— groups.

Polymerisation reactions

These reactions have been dealt with fully in Chapter 2. The only point to add here is that examination of the repeat unit will indicate whether polyaddition or polycondensation is required.

If the chain is an unbroken sequence of carbon atoms, then an alkene must be made to undergo polyaddition. The only other common example of this type is the group of polyethers made by the addition polymerisation of an epoxide:

Most of the condensation polymers are either polyesters or polyamides, which involve the joining of molecules with two functional groups. Some care is needed in examining a polymer if the repeat unit is not given. Thus

$$—CH_2CH_2CH_2CH_2CONHCH_2CH_2CH_2CH_2CONHCH_2CH_2CH_2CH_2CONH—$$

has the repeat unit

$$—NHCH_2CH_2CH_2CH_2CO—$$

and would be made by the polycondensation (probably by heat) of the single amino acid

$$H_2NCH_2CH_2CH_2CH_2CO_2H$$

whereas the similar, but not identical, polyamide

$$-CH_2CH_2CH_2CH_2CONHCH_2CH_2CH_2CH_2NHCOCH_2CH_2CH_2CH_2CONH-$$

has the repeat unit

$$-NHCH_2CH_2CH_2CH_2NHCOCH_2CH_2CH_2CH_2CO-$$

and would need to be made by the co-polymerisation of the following diamine and dicarboxylic acid:

$$H_2NCH_2CH_2CH_2CH_2NH_2 \qquad HO_2CCH_2CH_2CH_2CH_2CO_2H$$

Similar care must be used when examining the structure of polyesters. They, too, can be made by the polycondensation of a hydroxy acid, or, like terylene, by the co-polymerisation of a diol and a dicarboxylic acid.

Practical synthetic techniques

In *elementary* synthesis the variety of methods is small. Most reaction techniques are concerned with mixing and temperature control.

Mixing

Unlike the reactions of inorganic chemistry, those of organic chemistry often use immiscible liquid reactants, and it is thus necessary to shake or stir the mixture.

Shaking is normally only practicable in stoppered flasks for reactions that do not build up pressure or in flasks fitted with condensers for reflux (see below). Sometimes, when there is an appreciable difference in the densities of immiscible liquids, e.g. in the nitration of benzene, or when, as in the reduction of nitrobenzene to phenylamine, a dense solid is involved as well, vigorous shaking is the only feasible method of bringing the reactants together adequately.

A mechanical stirrer is normally used if the reaction takes an appreciable time (Figure 3.6). This may take the form of a motor-driven 'paddle', which dips into the reaction mixture, or, for reactions that do not need heating, a magnetic stirrer may be employed. The latter is simply a small iron bar coated with an unreactive plastic material (to prevent reaction with the iron or damage to the glass), which is spun round under the influence of a magnet that is rotated below the flask.

Temperature control

Compared with inorganic reactions, which are often ionic and very fast, most organic reactions are relatively slow. The formation of the transition states usually involves breaking of covalent bonds (homolytically or heterolytically), for which high activation energies are needed. Hence the reactions are often heated. Often reactions that begin vigorously, e.g. the nitration of benzene or the reduction of nitrobenzene, require heating to bring about completion. For

Figure 3.6 A magnetic stirrer in use

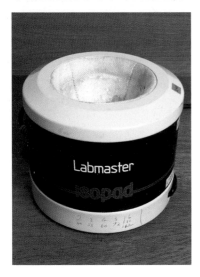

safety, this is usually done on a steam bath or by using an electric heating mantle (see Figure 3.7), but the heating brings another problem. Organic materials are usually volatile, to some extent, and heating the mixture would cause them to escape. Apart from the consequent reduction in yield, this has associated fire and health hazards. In order to prevent loss of materials, the heating is usually done under reflux (Figure 3.7). Here a condenser is fitted, often vertically, to the reaction flask so that condensed vapour is returned directly to the flask.

Cooling is often required, usually to prevent reactions becoming uncontrollable, e.g. the nitration of a compound such as cellulose can suddenly become an explosive oxidation if the heat of reaction is allowed to raise the temperature appreciably. In some reactions, temperature control is needed to prevent further reaction, e.g. the production of excessive amounts of dinitrobenzene when nitrating benzene. Such cooling is usually achieved by placing the reaction flask under a stream of cold water over the sink.

Figure 3.7 Boiling under reflux can be carried out safely using a heating mantle

Techniques for isolation of solids

The chosen technique usually depends on the solubility of the solid product in the reaction mixture. Insoluble products are usually isolated by filtration; sometimes they may be rendered insoluble and precipitated. Soluble solids may be isolated by evaporation, but this is uncommon from reaction mixtures (see below).

Filtration

In preparative inorganic chemistry, filtration is usually employed to remove small amounts of *unwanted* material from a liquid, e.g. undissolved solid from a solution or excess of a solid reactant from a liquid mixture. Recovery of the solid is not normally important and it is spread thinly over the surface of a large filter paper so as to give the fastest filtration. In organic chemistry, the solid is often the required product, and spreading it thinly would give large **mechanical losses**, a term used to describe material lost during physical operations. Here much material would be irrecoverable from the surface of the paper. However, a thick deposit of solid in a filter slows filtration down to an unacceptable rate.

The problem is overcome by using a **Büchner funnel** (Figure 3.8), or similar device, in which reduction of pressure below a perforated plate supporting the filter paper causes atmospheric pressure to drive the liquid through. Not only does this speed up the process, but also the pad of solid on the filter has much of the included liquid forced down into the receiving flask at the end – in common, though inaccurate, parlance it is 'sucked dry'. Modern funnels of this type are often made in three pieces: this assists in the removal of the cake of solid and makes cleaning of the funnel easier.

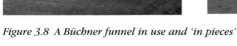

Figure 3.8 A Büchner funnel in use and 'in pieces'

It is important, during the formation of the solid, to allow it to form slowly; e.g. if the solid crystallises, the solution should be allowed to cool slowly. The larger particles so produced do not clog the filter. It is also important not to evacuate the receiving flask too strongly, especially at the start of filtration, because the unsupported areas of wet filter paper, over the perforations, can collapse.

Precipitation

Precipitation (followed by filtration) is frequently used to isolate solids that remain dissolved in a reaction mixture.

Precipitation may involve a chemical change, as in the precipitation of benzoic acid from its alkaline solution by a mineral acid, e.g. hydrochloric acid:

$$PhCO_2^-(aq) \quad + \quad H^+(aq) \quad \rightleftharpoons \quad PhCO_2H(s)$$

but it is more often brought about by the addition of water or, less commonly, other solvents. Most organic compounds are effectively insoluble in water, and if water is miscible with the reaction mixture (e.g. the reaction may have been carried out in ethanol), then slow addition of water will normally precipitate the organic product. Whilst this leaves inorganic materials in solution, it has the serious disadvantage that other organic materials are likely to be precipitated. The resulting solid may be sticky, intractable and difficult to filter.

Liquids are also occasionally separated in this way. After the nitration of benzene, when the mixture of nitrobenzene and mixed acids is poured into water, the nitrobenzene settles out below the (cloudy) aqueous acids. Any unchanged benzene and unwanted dinitrobenzene will, unfortunately, accompany the product.

Evaporation

Isolation of a solid from a reaction mixture by evaporation of a solvent is rare. All non-volatile components, unchanged reactants and other products, are left behind and purification is difficult. Evaporation is most frequently employed if a solid has first been removed from a (reaction) mixture by solvent extraction (see below) or chromatography (see below).

Evaporation is usually done in stages. First, the extract may be dried by the direct addition of a non-reactive drying agent. The filtered or decanted solution is then reduced in volume by simple distillation: this recovers the solvent for re-use and avoids environmental pollution and fire hazards caused by discarding it. The final stage depends on whether the desired material is a liquid or a solid at room temperature (see also the section on liquids below). If the product is a solid or involatile liquid, the last of the solvent is likely to be removed by evaporation under reduced pressure.

Purification of solids

Traditionally, solids are purified by recrystallisation from a solution. This, and less common methods such as distillation (for low-melting solids like ethanamide) or sublimation (for higher-melting solids), is suited to large-scale synthesis. An enormous variety of methods is available for small-scale purification: many are forms of chromatography (see below).

ORGANIC SYNTHESIS

Why is it helpful when purifying by recrystallisation if an impurity is much less or much more soluble than the desired compound?

Recrystallisation of solids

This term **recrystallised** is loosely used whether the solid has been previously crystallised or not. A suitable solvent must not react with the solid. The solubility of the solid should be high near the boiling point of the solvent and as low as possible at room temperature. If possible, the impurities should either be insoluble in it (unlikely) or very soluble in it. The solvent should not normally boil at a temperature above the melting point of the solid, since the latter may be initially precipitated as a liquid. This will then solidify in lumps, trapping solvent and impurities (dissolved in the solvent).

The compound for purification is dissolved in the minimum of hot solvent. The hot solution is filtered to remove insoluble matter. This may cool and cause premature precipitation, but the problem can usually be overcome by using a slight excess of solvent, a pre-heated funnel and a fluted filter paper (folded for fast filtering). Funnels with heating jackets can also be used (Figure 3.9). The hot solution is then allowed to crystallise in a conical flask with a loose stopper to keep out dust and dirt.

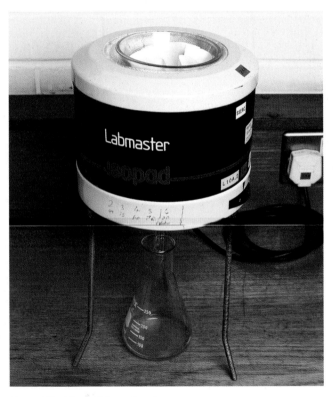

Figure 3.9 A heated funnel and a fluted filter paper

The crystalline solid is usually separated from the cold solvent by filtration using a Büchner funnel. There is always appreciable loss of the solid because of its solubility. This can be minimised by finally cooling the solution in a refrigerator if the impurities are likely to be in insufficient amount to saturate the solution at this temperature. When filtering, the remaining solution must be removed from the surface of the crystals or it will evaporate, leaving dissolved impurities. For this reason, it is usual to wash the solid on the filter with a *little*, usually ice-cold, solvent.

Recrystallisation is usually repeated until the material has a constant, sharp melting point.

If a solid is discoloured, recrystallisation often fails to remove all of the impurity responsible. Treating the hot solution to be crystallised with a little activated charcoal before hot filtration often removes the coloured impurity by adsorption. It will doubtless remove other impurities, too, but it will also cause some loss of the desired product.

Techniques for the isolation of liquids

Many reaction products are liquids. The desired component is usually isolated by distillation, sometimes preceded by solvent extraction.

Simple distillation

If the product is sufficiently different in boiling point from the rest of the reaction mixture, and does not form an **azeotrope**, simple distillation may be used. Thus, bromoethane may be prepared by the reaction of potassium bromide, ethanol, concentrated sulphuric acid and a little water. The boiling point of bromoethane (38°C) is very different from that of ethanol (78°C), water (100°C) and concentrated sulphuric acid (>300°C). Simple distillation removes the crude compound from the mixture, but it will be contaminated by small amounts of ethoxyethane (b.p. 35°C), which is always formed in this reaction, and by dissolved hydrogen bromide and perhaps a trace of volatile bromine.

Sometimes a liquid will be removed from an aqueous mixture by solvent extraction (see below). Thus, after steam distillation (see below), phenylamine is extracted from the mixture with water by extraction with ethoxyethane ('ether'). The extract is then dried and the extracting solvent and product are separated by distillation.

Steam distillation

Steam distillation (Figure 3.10) is occasionally a preliminary step in the isolation of a product. The conditions seriously limit its use. The liquid to be isolated should be immiscible with, or only slightly soluble in, water. It would normally be present in an aqueous reaction mixture with no appreciable amounts of other water-immiscible, volatile organic compounds. In such circumstances, it is very useful for separating the organic product from large amounts of soluble inorganic matter.

Figure 3.10 Steam distillation in the laboratory

In Chapter 5 we look at the vapour pressures of liquid mixtures and see how they vary with composition. If two liquids are immiscible, the situation is a very simple one: the vapour pressure of the mixture is the sum of the separate vapour pressures of the pure liquids, i.e. they each behave as if the other is not present.

As the temperature of a mixture of two immiscible liquids is raised, the total vapour pressure *must* reach atmospheric pressure before that of either component alone. The boiling point of the mixture must, therefore, be lower than that of the lower-boiling liquid.

If water is one of the two liquids, as in steam distillation, then distillation must occur at a temperature of less than 100°C, however high the boiling point of the other component.

Thus, in the steam distillation of phenylamine at normal atmospheric pressure, distillation occurs at about 98°C because, although water has a vapour pressure of about 93 kPa at this temperature, the much less volatile phenylamine (b.p. 184°C) has a vapour pressure of 7 kPa and raises the total pressure to 100 kPa. It is necessary to collect quite a large volume of the distillate after the last phenylamine has been seen as oily droplets because it is slightly soluble in water. The last of the phenylamine obeys Raoult's law, has a much lower vapour pressure and is too soluble to precipitate in the condensed distillate.

ORGANIC SYNTHESIS

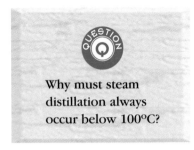

Why must steam distillation always occur below 100°C?

Figure 3.11 An extraction funnel containing two immiscible liquids

Why must the stopper be removed from a separating funnel before opening the tap to run off the contents?

There still remains the problem of separating the immiscible liquid from the water in the distillate. If the organic product is completely insoluble in water, this can be done in a separating funnel: the product will still need to be dried and redistilled. In the example of phenylamine, as in many other preparations, the small but appreciable solubility of the product in water necessitates the use of solvent extraction (see below) before purification.

Steam distillation has been used commercially to extract fragrant oils from flower petals, etc., which might tend to undergo chemical changes, e.g. isomerisation, at higher temperatures. Protection from thermal decomposition, oxidation, etc., is far more efficiently provided by vacuum distillation, and this has tended to take the place of steam distillation where aqueous mixtures are avoidable. Phenylamine boils at 184°C without decomposition. It may be steam distilled at 98°C as a convenient method of dealing with an aqueous mixture. Whilst it could be vacuum distilled at 68°C and 1.3 kPa pressure, there is little advantage to the use of this technique here.

Solvent extraction

It is often necessary to purify a compound that is wholly, or partially (as in the example of phenylamine above), soluble in water. If the mixture was obtained by steam distillation, it cannot be separated by further distillation. The desired compound is usually first obtained as a more concentrated solution in a solvent which is immiscible with water and which can be separated from the compound by distillation, i.e. the solvent has a very different boiling point (usually lower) and does not form an azeotropic mixture (see Chapter 5). A common extraction solvent is ethoxyethane or 'ether' (b.p. 35°C). 'Salting out' (see opposite page) may be used to reduce the solubility of the compound in water.

The aqueous solution (of the desired compound) is shaken in a stoppered separating funnel with the extracting solvent (Figure 3.11). The funnel should be inverted and the tap opened momentarily after the first shake in order to release the slight internal pressure. The funnel is held steady in a suitable clamp or stand whilst the layers are allowed to separate and, after removing the stopper, they are run out through the tap into separate vessels. If the solvent is more dense than water, only the lower layer need be run off.

A second portion of solvent is added to the funnel with the depleted aqueous layer and the process is repeated. It may be shown mathematically that it is more efficient to use a given volume of extracting solvent in several successive portions rather than all at once.

The extract is then dried by the addition of a suitable drying agent (in a stoppered flask). This is most commonly granular anhydrous calcium chloride or anhydrous magnesium sulphate. If the desired organic compound reacts with this (as does phenylamine), then other drying agents such as potassium hydroxide pellets or anhydrous sodium sulphate need to be used.

Finally, the dried extract is separated from the drying agent by decanting or filtering and the product is then purified by distilling off the extraction solvent, which is collected for re-use, and distillation (or, in the case of a solid, by recrystallisation) of the desired compound.

Salting out

The more polar a solute, the more effectively water competes with any immiscible solvent used to extract the solute, and the less efficient is the extraction. The solubility of organic compounds in water is markedly reduced by the addition of a soluble electrolyte. Common salt, sodium chloride, is cheap, effective and insoluble in organic extraction solvents. If the solubility of a compound in water poses a serious problem, as in the steam distillate containing phenylamine above, saturation of the aqueous solution with salt produces an immediate white precipitate (or emulsion) of oily droplets. This is called 'salting out'. It is usually followed by solvent extraction.

Washing

Often a crude, water-immiscible liquid product contains impurities that can be removed by washing with water or an aqueous reagent. Nitric and sulphuric acids in crude nitrobenzene may be removed by washing with water. Dissolved hydrogen bromide can be removed from crude bromoethane by washing with aqueous sodium carbonate. The operation is carried out by mixing the crude product and the washing liquid in a separating funnel, shaking well and allowing to stand so that the two liquids separate. It is a very important safety precaution when washing with aqueous sodium carbonate first to invert the stoppered separating funnel and open the tap to release the pressure of evolved carbon dioxide. Mixing should then be done with great care, opening the tap of the inverted funnel frequently to release any gas.

Chromatography

First used to separate coloured solids in solution, e.g. leaf pigments in petrol, this method now has many forms. Essentially a moving phase (e.g. a solvent containing the substance to be purified, separated or simply identified) passes over a stationary phase (e.g. paper, chalk or alumina).

Each substance in the moving phase, e.g. each solute in the solvent (which itself may be ignored), has a different affinity for the stationary phase, and equilibria are set up between the moving substance (in solution) and that retained by the stationary phase. A component, **A**, that is strongly attracted to the stationary phase moves along only very slowly, because any **A** that returns to the moving phase is immediately removed from it at the next free 'site' it encounters. A component, **B**, that has little affinity for the stationary phase tends to stay in and move along with the moving phase.

Some common types of chromatography are given in Table 3.1.

Table 3.1 *The phases in various types of chromatography*

Moving phase	Stationary phase	Type of chromatography
A liquid solvent	Paper	Paper chromatography
	Alumina, chalk, etc	Adsorption chromatography
	Moist silica gel	Partition chromatography
	Ion-exchange resin	Ion-exchange chromatography
A 'carrier' gas, e.g. nitrogen	Solid	Gas chromatography
	Porous solid plus viscous liquid	Gas-liquid chromatography (GLC)

4 Organic analysis and structure determination

The methods used by organic chemists to find the identity of a simple compound or to find the structure of an unknown compound in the first half of the twentieth century differed little from those in the nineteenth century. The second half of the twentieth century has seen a complete revolution in technique.

Before the spectroscopic revolution

Before the advent of spectroscopy, the compound had to be isolated in a pure condition, still an essential requirement when examining a new compound, but techniques of purification have been greatly improved. Solids were separated by solvent extraction and fractional crystallisation; liquids were purified by some form of distillation. Large quantities of the order of a gram or more were needed, and the methods of purification gave large mechanical losses.

The first need was to establish the qualitative composition (C, H, O – and what else?) and then the quantitative composition of the compound. Destructive methods were used, e.g. burning a sample of known mass and absorbing and weighing the water and carbon dioxide produced. Further destruction of the precious sample allowed determination of the percentage of nitrogen or sulphur. In skilled hands, reliable results were given, but experimental errors would lend uncertainty to the empirical formulae of complicated compounds like cholesterol, $C_{27}H_{48}O$ (C = 83.5%, H = 12.4%), which might mistakenly be given a formula like $C_{27}H_{47}O$ (C = 83.3%, H = 12.2%) or $C_{27}H_{46}O$ (C = 83.1%, H = 11.9%).

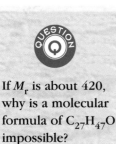

If M_r is about 420, why is a molecular formula of $C_{27}H_{47}O$ impossible?

To convert the empirical formula to a molecular formula, a relative molecular mass had to be determined. The methods used were not destructive, but it was not always easy or possible to recover the compound: their main drawback was lack of accuracy. Errors of 10% are not serious if the problem is to decide whether cholesterol has the formula $C_{27}H_{48}O$ ($M_r = 388$) or $C_{54}H_{96}O_2$ ($M_r = 776$): an experimental result of $M_r = 420$ clearly indicates the former. However, to decide whether a sugar with the empirical formula CH_2O was a pentose $C_5H_{10}O_5$ ($M_r = 150$) or a hexose $C_6H_{12}O_6$ ($M_r = 180$) would prove more difficult if the experimental method gave a value of 165.

A long search for functional groups using bromine water, potassium manganate(VII), Fehling's solution, etc., slowly built up a picture of the molecule at the same time as much of the compound was destroyed! You can imagine the problems that faced the organic chemist earlier in this century when deciding how best to use the small amount of material in his or her possession.

In 1935, Doisy processed 1.5 tonnes of sows' ovaries to obtain 12 mg of oestradiol. In his time, the only hope of determining the structure of such a compound with such an amount was to show that it was identical with one already known (see below).

If a compound did not appear to be identical with anything already known, the compound had to be broken down chemically into recognisable molecular pieces, or degraded, by 'nibbling off' one functional group after another, into something recognisable. All the problems of loss of material and poor yields, of separation and purification, began again.

When a molecule or molecular fragment was thought to be familiar, its properties had to be compared with known compounds. The melting point of a solid or the boiling point and refractive index of a liquid had to be found. But millions of organic compounds exist with melting points and boiling points in the practical range of, say, 20 to 300°C, and that means that thousands are occupying every degree of the scale.

Solids were easier to identify than liquids. The probable identity of a solid of known melting point could be confirmed with a fair degree of certainty by doing a 'mixed melting point' with a genuine sample. Thus an aromatic carboxylic acid (X), $C_8H_8O_2$, might be one of the following:

A	**B**	**C**	**D**
m.p 180°C	111°C	108°C	76°C

An observed melting point of 108°C would almost certainly mean that **X** was 2-methylbenzenecarboxylic acid (**C**, m.p. 108°C), but the presence of a very small amount of impurity in **X** might have lowered its m.p., and the possibility that **X** was 3-methylbenzenecarboxylic acid (**B**, m.p. 111°C) could not be ruled out. (Had the determined m.p. of **X** been 111°C, however, C would be most unlikely.) Small samples of **X** would be separately mixed with an equal bulk of compounds **B** and **C**, and the melting point of the mixtures would be determined. If the mixture with **B** began to melt at, say, 95°C but the m.p. of the mixture with **C** was largely unchanged, the unknown compound, **X**, would almost certainly be **C**. You *could* decide between these two possible structures by oxidation of **X** and determination of the m.p. of the oxidation product, but it would be more trouble and would require more material.

What would you use to oxidise X and what would you expect to get from the two possible structures?

Liquids were usually more difficult to identify than solids. To begin with, accurate boiling points are more difficult to determine and required more material than melting points: mechanical losses tend to be larger when handling liquids. If a liquid molecular fragment (**Y**), $C_7H_{12}O$, was recognised to be a saturated ketone with a boiling point of 170± 1°C, it might be 3-methyl*cyclo*hexanone (**E**) or 4-methyl*cyclo*hexanone (**F**). **Derivatives** were prepared, e.g. phenylhydrazones (**G** and **H**). These solids could be narrowed down to a few possibilities by considering their melting points in addition to the information already known.

E
b.p. 170°C

F
b.p. 171°C

G
m.p. 94°C

H
m.p. 110°C

If the phenylhydrazone of the unknown compound had a melting point of 94°C, that would indicate that **Y** was 3-methyl*cyclo*hexanone (**E**). To confirm the identity, either the 2,4-dinitrophenylhydrazone of a known sample of **E** would be prepared and a mixed melting point carried out, *or* a second derivative, e.g. the 2,4-dinitrophenylhydrazone, would be prepared.

If **Y** (= **E**) had been obtained by the oxidation of a double bond in a more complicated molecule, e.g. by the use of ozone (trioxygen), and the compound formed simultaneously had been butanone, the chemist then had to find a means of deciding how the two fragments fitted together. Do they form **I** or **J**?

What kind of isomers are I and J?

Sometimes, when structures were broken down chemically, rearrangements of the skeleton occurred and chemists were misled by the isomers that they isolated.

Whilst chemical methods like these are now largely displaced by spectroscopy, *chemical* analysis is still indispensable in certain fields. Unbelievably rapid methods have been devised for the automatic sequencing of bases in DNA, and for the amino acids in proteins, which replace methods that took, literally, years. However, these methods are based on chemical reactions.

Spectroscopy

Spectroscopy has revolutionised chemistry in the second half of the twentieth century. The main reasons why it is so superior to the classical 'chemical' methods of structure determination, analysis and identification are that:

- Results are obtained quickly.

- Only minute quantities of materials (milligram quantities) are required.

- Methods are often non-destructive.

- Results (e.g. M_r) are usually very precise.

The four branches of spectroscopy most useful to the organic chemist are indicated in Figure 4.1, along with their particular ranges of application. The older techniques of ultra-violet (UV) and infra-red (IR) are gradually being superseded for structure determination by those on the right-hand side, which were technically very difficult to introduce and thus became available comparatively late in the twentieth century.

The London Examinations syllabus expects a limited knowledge of the applications of infra-red and mass spectrometry to the analysis of organic compounds. Only these techniques will be discussed in the main part of this book, but see Appendix, page 87.

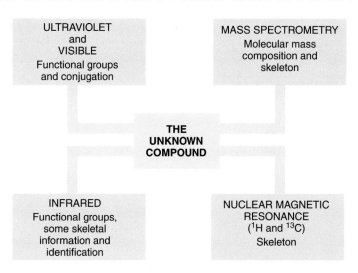

Figure 4.1 Four branches of spectroscopy that the organic chemist finds most useful

Absorption spectra

IR spectrometers measure the amount of electromagnetic radiation transmitted by a compound (or a solution of that compound). Two identical beams of IR radiation are produced. One beam is passed through a compound and the other is passed through air, and the emerging beams are compared.

When an **isolated atom** (or ion) of an element absorbs radiation (usually UV), it does so at a precise frequency (or wavelength). As a result, the atom is raised from one electronic state to a more excited state. The energy levels of these two states are precisely defined (E_0 and E_1) and so, therefore, is their difference ΔE (Figure 4.2). This produces the sharp line spectra of atoms (see *Structure, Bonding and the Periodic Table*).

Now whilst the electronic levels of isolated atoms are precise, those of molecules are grouped about ideal values, because the molecules are in a variety of states of mechanical vibration and distortion which increase or decrease the total energy. Instead of a precise line in the spectrum of the molecule, a **band** of absorption is produced, centred about the most common energy difference (Figure 4.3). The wavelength of maximum absorption may also be shifted slightly by the environment of the molecule, e.g. the solvent used to dissolve it.

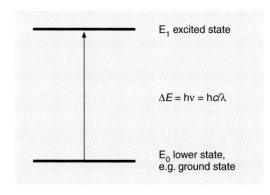

Figure 4.2 Formation of sharp lines in atomic spectra

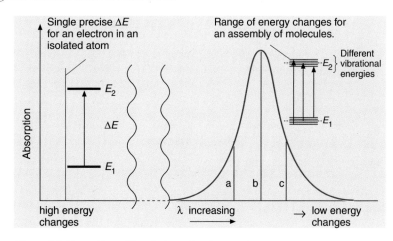

Figure 4.3 Formation of bands in molecular spectra

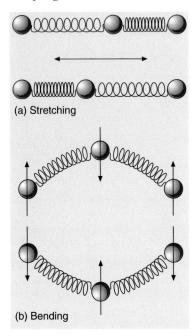

Figure 4.4 *Vibrations of molecules can be thought of in terms of balls and springs*

(a) Stretching

(b) Bending

Infra-red spectroscopy

Introduction

The energy transitions responsible for infra-red absorption (or emission) are concerned with the mechanical vibrations of molecules, e.g. stretching or several kinds of bending (Figure 4.4).

The stretching of a C—H bond in an alkane absorbs at a frequency of about $8.7 \times 10^{13} \, s^{-1}$. Numbers like this are not easy to write or talk about, and spectroscopists have adopted the use of the **wave-number** to describe the frequency of maximum absorption in the spectrum. If a wave were to be emitted for exactly one second, then the wave train would be 3×10^{10} cm long (the speed of light is $3 \times 10^{10} \, cm \, s^{-1}$). The wave-number is the number of wave-lengths in 1 cm. In Figure 4.5, drawn for simplicity, the wave-number would be $5 \, cm^{-1}$ – far outside the IR region, which, for practical purposes, extends from about 4000 to 700 cm^{-1}.

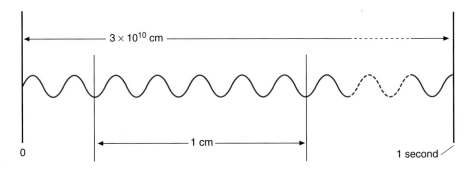

3×10^{10} cm

1 cm

0   1 second

Figure 4.5 *How to think of wave-number*

Spectra are usually drawn showing transmittance rather than absorption, and hence the 'peaks' are upside-down. For purely historical reasons, the wave-number decreases from left to right (Figure 4.6).

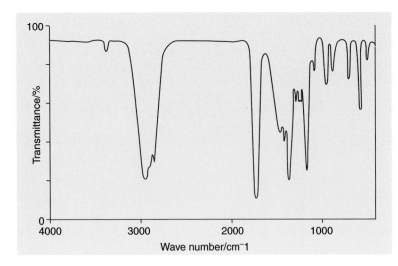

Figure 4.6 *A typical IR spectrum (that of pentan-2-one)*

Any given bond within a molecule can be stretched or bent in a variety of ways. Hence a given bond can absorb at several different frequencies. Also, as in other vibrations (e.g. in stringed instruments), overtones occur. This makes IR spectra very complicated. Organic chemists are not so much interested in the type of vibration, e.g. stretching or bending, causing a particular absorption but rather in the ability to associate particular absorption frequencies with *particular bonds in different environments*. Thus a C≡C bond in ethene (Figure 4.7) is like a spring with 14 mass units at each end. The 'spring' would have a natural period of vibration (stretching or bending).

The same C=C double bond ('spring') would be expected to have different mechanical properties in oleic acid (*cis*-octadec-9-enoic acid) (**A**), with a mass of over 100 units on each end, or in *cyclo*hexene (**B**), where the double bond or 'spring' is restrained by the rest of the molecule (Figure 4.8). In a cyclic molecule, the rest of the molecule has to distort with every vibration of the 'spring', and the period and energy required are altered.

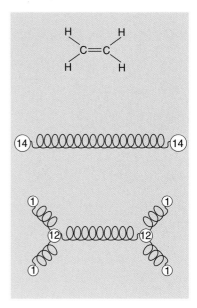

Figure 4.7 Ethene can be thought of as a spring with 14 mass units at each end

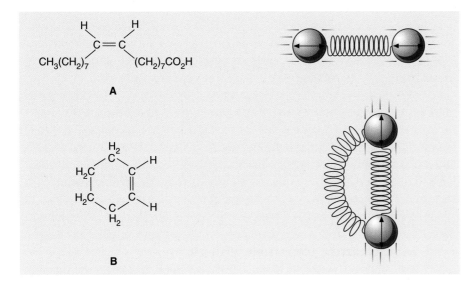

Figure 4.8 The same bonds in different molecules will have different mechanical properties and so have different frequencies and spectra

Divisions of the IR spectrum

The spectrum can be divided into two working parts, the **band region** and the **fingerprint region** (Figure 4.9).

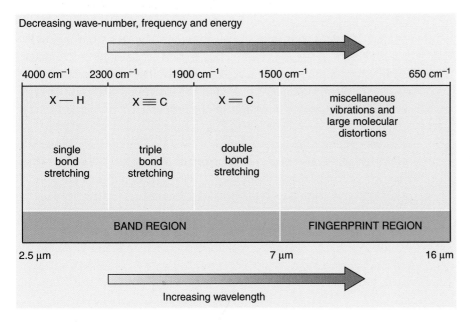

Figure 4.9 The regions of the IR spectrum

ORGANIC ANALYSIS AND STRUCTURE DETERMINATION

Plotting the IR spectrum

This is now largely an automatic process. 'IR machines' have been a routine part of general laboratory equipment since the mid-1950s.

Identifying a compound with IR

IR spectra are most valuable for the identification of compounds by comparison of the spectrum of the unknown with those of likely possibilities. Vast libraries of such spectra are maintained by research laboratories, and 'atlases' of these spectra have been marketed in books and in electronic format, e.g. CD-ROMs. This method of identification is far more reliable than the use of melting points, mixed melting points, boiling points and other physical properties.

Identification is not just a matter of comparing the peaks caused by known functional groups, e.g. C$=$O or C$=$C. If a known carbonyl compound is being identified, it will be no surprise to find an absorption peak associated with the C$=$O bond! Rather, the test is to match the absorption in a complex region between 1400 and 1800 cm^{-1} called, for obvious reasons, the fingerprint region. In this region, a huge range of skeletal vibrations produce an absorption pattern of great complexity, which is unique to a given compound.

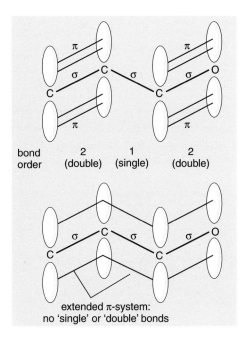

bond order

Figure 4.10 Extended π-system in an unsaturated ketone

Investigating structure with IR

The process consists, in essence, of matching the peaks in the **band region** of the spectrum with particular features, e.g. C$=$O, C—O—C, O—H, to see which of the possible isomers of a compound is most likely. Shifts in the peak frequencies, sometimes slight, give clues about the environment of the functional group. Even the C—H absorptions of terminal CH$_3$— and internal —CH$_2$— are slightly different. Conjugation of double bonds often produces large shifts. Thus the C$=$O absorption of an aliphatic ketone is normally found at about 1725–1705 cm^{-1} and that of the C$=$C in a simple alkene is in the region of 1680–1620 cm^{-1}. But in an unsaturated ketone, in which these two π-systems are conjugated to produce an extended π-system (Figure 4.10), the bond orders of the C$=$C, C$=$O and intervening C—C cease to be 2, 2 and 1, respectively, and the mechanical properties of the system are altered. The C$=$O absorption might move to 1685–1665 cm^{-1} and the C$=$C absorption frequency would similarly be reduced.

The absorption of the carbonyl group, C$=$O, also depends (to a lesser extent) on whether it is part of an aliphatic aldehyde (1740–1720 cm^{-1}), a ketone (1730–1710 cm^{-1}), an ester (1750–1730 cm^{-1}), an acid (1725–1700 cm^{-1}) or an amide (1700–1650 cm^{-1}).

The fingerprint region is not of much use in the analytical determination of structure until final identification by matching spectra is reached. However, the absence of an expected band in the fingerprint region can often be diagnostic. For example, the absence of a band at about 1380 cm^{-1} suggests the *absence* of terminal CH$_3$— groups, but the *presence* of such a band might be due to one of a number of causes and is not a reliable indicator.

Consider three of the many possible isomers of $C_5H_{10}O$, labelled as **A**, **B** and **C** below:

$$H_2C\!\!=\!\!CHCH_2OCH_2CH_3$$

B

$$\underset{\textstyle CH_3CH_2CCH_2CH_3}{\overset{\textstyle O}{\overset{\|}{}}}$$

C

A

B should show C=C absorption near 1650 cm⁻¹ whereas C should show C=O absorption near 1710 cm⁻¹: both of these should show terminal CH₃— absorption near 1380 cm⁻¹. On the other hand, A should show none of these (but, remember, the *presence* of a band in the fingerprint region is not a reliable indicator of the *presence* of a bond).

It would be much more difficult, if not impossible, to distinguish **C** from **D**, $CH_3CH_2CH_2COCH_3$ (whose IR spectrum is shown in Figure 4.6), without access to predetermined spectra of the pure compounds, but then a simple chemical test would do that. Of course, C=C and C=O, in this case, could have been found by simple chemical tests. A chemist does not use one weapon alone, from the armoury, to fight a battle.

It is impossible, in an elementary treatment such as this, to give a comprehensive list of absorption frequencies. Some common ones are given in Table 4.1, but you may find rather different values if you look up the ranges in detailed works on spectroscopy.

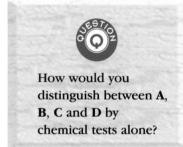

QUESTION

How would you distinguish between **A**, **B**, **C** and **D** by chemical tests alone?

Table 4.1 *Some common IR absorption frequency ranges*

Bond	Approximate range of frequencies/cm⁻¹	Comments
C—H	3000–2850	in alkanes
C—H	3100–3000	in alkanes and aromatic rings
N—H	3500–3300	primary amines; dependent on hydrogen-bonding
O—H	3600–3300	broad bands; very dependent on hydrogen-bonding, which shifts the absorption to lower frequency (lower energy), i.e. to the right, sometimes beyond the range given
C—O	1200–1150	in esters
C—Cl	800–600	
C—Br	600–500	
C—I	550–450	
C=C	1680–1620	
C=O	1750–1680	
C≡C	2260–2150	
C≡N	2260–2200	

ORGANIC ANALYSIS AND STRUCTURE DETERMINATION
Mass spectrometry

Introduction
A brief description of a (low-resolution) mass spectrometer has been given in *Structure, Bonding and the Periodic Table*. The instrument is used in organic chemistry principally for the determination of molecular masses, chemical formulae and structures. This form of spectrometry differs from infra-red (IR), ultra-violet (UV) and nuclear magnetic resonance (NMR) in that it does not involve the measurement of absorption of electromagnetic radiation.

Mass spectrometers measure the ratio of mass to charge for positive ions and are calibrated as if they measured mass alone, in atomic mass units. Loosely, therefore, they are said to measure mass, i.e. for convenience, reference to charge is omitted. But it should always be borne in mind that, *in principle*, they measure the mass/charge ratio and, should an ion become doubly charged, a comparatively rare occurrence, it would appear to have half the true mass.

The spectrum is plotted as relative abundance of an ion (y-axis) against mass/charge ratio (x-axis). The x-axis is normally labelled m/e or m/z. In this book we shall use m/z, where z is the number of (electronic) charges (normally 1, which 'disappears'): e has a definite value, which is not 1, and to use true values of m/e would give numbers that are not the same as (or simple sub-multiples of) the relative mass of the particle.

Formation of the spectrum
The common method of generating the positive ions is to vaporise a minute sample of the compound by heating it on a probe in the ionisation chamber (Figure 4.11), which, like all the internal parts of the spectrometer, is highly evacuated. A volatile liquid may simply be allowed to enter this part of the instrument. A heated filament releases electrons, which are drawn across the ionisation chamber to an anode on the other side of the sample vapour. The fast electrons from the filament 'knock out' electrons from the molecules of sample, and the positive ions generated are drawn across the chamber by a weak electric field into a second accelerator chamber through a slit. Once there, the positive ions accelerate rapidly in a strong electric field and emerge through a second slit into a strong uniform magnetic field across a circular cavity, often a 'D' section. Their charge forces them round the curve of the 'D', and only if there is a perfect match between charge/mass ratio and magnetic field will they emerge through the final analyser slit and be detected. The magnetic field (or accelerating voltage) is gradually changed to allow for different masses across the range of the spectrum.

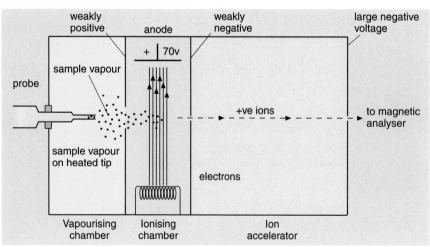

Figure 4.11 Ion production by electron bombardment in a mass spectrometer

The nature of the ion

The normal initial reaction of the molecule will be to form a positive ion by loss of one of its electrons:

$$M \; + \; e^- \; \rightarrow \; M^+ \; + \; 2e^-$$

	high		low
	energy		energy

The species formed is called the **molecular ion**, and its existence allows the relative molecular mass to be determined. In a high-resolution machine, it may permit the determination of the molecular formula (see below). We shall represent the mass/charge ratio for this ion by M (or M/z) and for other ions by m (or m/z).

When the sample is ionised in this way, not all the molecular ions survive. Breakdown of the molecular ion in this way is called fragmentation. The instability of the molecular ion arises (like the instability of most chemical species) from two causes:

- The ion has a higher (chemical) energy content than alternative particles into which it can break down (thermodynamic instability).

- The ion has absorbed a large amount of energy from the collision with the ionising electron, which it has retained in the form of vibrations. This vibrational energy may well exceed the necessary activation energy to disrupt the structure of the ion (kinetic instability).

In some cases the molecular ion is undetectable. At the other extreme, many aromatic compounds give very stable molecular ions. Generally, the bigger the molecule, the more likely it is to fragment. Since a knowledge of the molecular mass is crucial to structure determination, much of the progress of the last twenty years has been made by the use of more sophisticated methods of producing the molecular ion than the crude method of electron bombardment.

The nature of fragmentation

Fragmentation is a rapid, unimolecular process: it is highly unlikely that collision with other molecules would occur at such low pressures and the ions themselves are mutually repulsive.

In simple 'bench' chemistry, if lead(II) nitrate is heated in a test-tube, three molecular species are almost exclusively formed:

$$2Pb(NO_3)_2(s) \; \rightarrow \; 2PbO(s) \; + \; 4NO_2(g) \; + \; O_2(g)$$

At very high temperatures we might get some $NO(g)$ as well. We do not get NO_3, Pb or PbN_2 for sound thermodynamic and chemical reasons.

In a similar way, the unimolecular decomposition of the molecular ion gives rise to a chemically well defined set of fragments, which themselves may break down further in a predictable way. Experience has allowed chemists to deduce rules for this fragmentation, though the number and nature of the fragments is, to some extent, dependent on the energy of the ionising electrons. We can do no more than hint at these, because we are concerned with the synthesis of the whole molecule from its fragments.

The molecular ion may break down in several ways. The most obvious limitation is that it rarely loses parts from the middle alone. Thus a molecular ion, $M^+ = (m_1 m_2 m_3)^+$, where m_1, m_2 and m_3 are continuous parts of a (carbon) chain, might break down as

$$(m_1 m_2 m_3)^+ \rightarrow (m_1 + m_2 + m_3)^+$$
$$\text{or} \quad \rightarrow (m_1 + m_2 m_3)^+$$
$$\text{or} \quad \rightarrow (m_1 m_2 + m_3)^+$$

but not as

$$(m_1 m_2 m_3)^+ \rightarrow (m_1 m_3 + m_2)^+$$

Only one fragment carries the positive charge: the other fragment may be a radical (split off by homolytic cleavage of a bond) or may be a stable molecule such as H_2, H_2O or $H_2C{=}CH_2$. The carrier of the charge is not randomly chosen but is predictable, and the neutral fragments, whether radicals or molecules, are not detected.

This means that if a molecular ion of mass 100 gives a positive fragment of mass 60, it may not give the complementary ion of mass 40. If it does give a positive ion of mass 40, it may be a smaller part of the ion of mass 60 and not the rest of the molecule.

The likelihood of formation of different positive ion fragments depends on their relative stabilities. Like carbocations (carbonium ions) in S_N1 reactions, the fragments increase in stability as the positive charge is placed on a primary, secondary or tertiary carbon atom. Thus when fragmentation of a hydrocarbon chain occurs, the least likely fragment is CH_3^+ and the least likely peak is at $m = 15$. Thus the absence of a peak at $m = 15$ by no means indicates the absence of a terminal methyl group: this is in complete contrast to the IR spectrum.

If fragmentation occurs very soon after formation of the molecular ion in the ionisation chamber, before the ion passes into the accelerator, then a clean separation of the fragments will occur. A few ions will fragment whilst in the ion accelerator or the magnetic field. In such cases the positive ion produced will be lost or detected in an inappropriate part of the spectrum. This mistaken identity is not the norm, and the few ions that are detected in the wrong part of the spectrum give rise to a relatively small amount of noise.

Since the *shape* of the peaks is largely due to instrumental defects and 'noise', and the *position* of the maximum and the area of the peak are all-important, the output of the (low-resolution) machine is passed though a computer and printed as a stick-diagram showing intensity (number of ions) against (nearest) mass

Molecular ion
This is the ion formed from the molecule by the loss of one electron.

number. The computer can be programmed to ignore a preset low level of intensity, e.g. 0.5%, thereby eliminating the 'noise'. The most intense peak, called the **base peak**, is given the value of 100 and the rest are scaled accordingly.

Isotope peaks

Methanol, CH_3OH, contains three elements, each of which has more than one isotope in the naturally occurring mixture. The most common methanol molecule will be made up of the most abundant isotopes (Table 4.2), carbon-12 (^{12}C), hydrogen (^1H) and oxygen-16 (^{16}O), and will have $M_r = 32$.

However, it is possible to find a molecule, $^{13}C^2H_3^{18}O^2H$, $M_r = 39$. The chance of doing this is about 1 in $90 \times (6700)^4 \times 500 = 1$ in 10^{20}: a few thousand molecules in every mole of methanol. This would be lost in the noise of even the most sophisticated mass spectrometer. Only $^{13}CH_3OH$, with a mass of 33, would appear as a tiny peak at $M = 33$, commonly referred to as '$M + 1$', with an intensity of about 1% of the peak at $M = 32$. The molecular ion peak is the one resulting from a molecule made up of the commonest (and usually lightest) isotopes. For a molecule with n carbon atoms, the intensity of the $M + 1$ peak is about n% of the intensity of the molecular ion peak. In elementary questions about mass spectra, it is often the practice to 'clean up' the spectrum by removing such minor peaks.

Peak patterns in the absence of halogens

Peaks, especially the base peak since it is the most intense, usually show peaks at $m + 1$ and even $m + 2$ because of the isotope effects described above. This is shown in Figure 4.12. In methane, CH_4, the molecular ion would show a peak at $M + 1$ ($= 17$) about 1% [theoretically $(1.1 \times 100/98.9) = 1.11$%] of the intensity of the peak at M. The molecular ion of ethane, C_2H_6, is twice as likely to have one ^{13}C atom; and the molecular ion for decane, $C_{10}H_{22}$, is ten times as likely, so the peak at $M + 1$ for decane should be about 11% of the intensity

Base peak
This is the most intense peak in the spectrum, which is arbitrarily given an intensity value of 100.

Table 4.2 *Some common isotopes*

Element	Symbol	Mass number	Main natural isotopes Abundance (%)	Approx. ratio
Carbon	^{12}C	12	98.9	90:1
	^{13}C	13	1.1	
Hydrogen	^1H	1	99.985	6700:1
(deuterium)	^2H	2	0.015	
Oxygen	^{16}O	16	99.8	500:1
	^{18}O	18	0.2	
Nitrogen	^{14}N	14	99.63	250:1
	^{15}N	15	0.37	
Chlorine	^{35}Cl	35	75.5	3:1
	^{37}Cl	37	24.5	
Bromine	^{79}Br	79	50.5	1:1
	^{81}Br	81	49.5	

of that at M. On the other hand, the bigger the molecule (unless aromatic), the less likely is the molecular ion to survive, hence the smaller will be the molecular ion peak and its growing isotopic companion.

Figure 4.12 Small peaks at M+1 caused by ^{13}C isotope

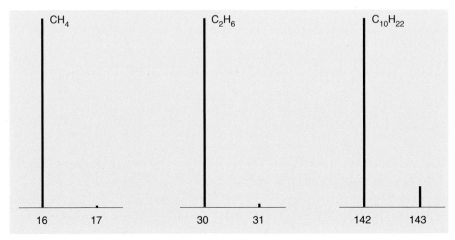

Peak patterns in the presence of halogens

Reference to the table of isotopes (Table 4.2) shows that, whilst ^{13}C exerts a detectable influence on the spectrum, the presence of chlorine or bromine results in large isotope effects.

If one atom of bromine is present in an ion fragment, then the peak for that fragment will be a doublet of equal intensity separated by 2 mass units. If two atoms of bromine are present in a fragment, it will give rise to a triplet (Figure 4.13). Since the four possible arrangements:

$$[79 \; + \; 79] \quad [79 \; + \; 81] \quad [81 \; + \; 79] \quad [81 \; + \; 81]$$

are equally probable, then the peaks at m, $m + 2$ and $m + 4$ will be in the ratio 1:2:1. It is thus immediately obvious if the molecular ion has two bromine atoms and which fragments have retained both, one or neither of them.

High-resolution spectrometry and isotopes

With the exception of the standard, $^{12}C = 12.00000$, isotopes never have integer relative atomic masses (Table 4.3).

Table 4.3 Some relative atomic masses

Element	Mass number of isotope	Accurate atomic mass
Hydrogen	1	1.00783
Carbon	12	12.00000
Nitrogen	14	14.0031
Oxygen	16	15.9949
Sulphur	32	31.9721
Chlorine	35	34.9689
Bromine	79	78.9183

Thus, whilst ethanoic acid, CH_3CO_2H or $C_2H_4O_2$, and propanol, $CH_3CH_2CH_2OH$ or C_3H_8O, both appear to have identical M_r for most purposes, the molecular ions of these species will have masses of 60.0211 and 60.0575. This difference is clearly shown in a high-resolution instrument. A simple computer program will evaluate the possible molecular formulae given a precise value for the mass of the molecular ion – and all this using quantities of the order of a milligram.

Building a structure from fragments

This is essentially a jig-saw puzzle with some of the pieces missing. Increasingly, mass spectrometry is playing a supporting role to NMR in the determination of complicated structures rather than leading the research.

Some important points to remember:

- Two fragments of mass greater than $M_r/2$ must overlap and their difference may represent a 'central' fragment.

- Any fragment of mass m is likely to be matched by a fragment of mass ($M_r - m$) even if this is not present in the spectrum, e.g. terminal methyl groups.

- Peaks differing by 14 mass units usually represent chain length differences of —CH_2—, but it is not certain that the less massive (lower m/z) of two adjacent principal peaks has been formed from the more massive one.

- Doublets and triplets are particularly important in establishing the chlorine or bromine content of fragments. Iodine has only one natural species of atom.

- Aromatic fragments (e.g. $m = 77$ for Ph^+) are particularly stable. Methyl fragments ($m = 15$) are unlikely to be found unless the chain is highly branched, i.e. the number of potential methyl ions compensates for the low probability of their formation. Hydrocarbon chains, in the absence of a heteroatom, tend to give tertiary rather than secondary carbocations; if these are not possible, then the fragmentation of a 'straight chain' (into the less probable primary carbocations) is fairly random.

- Carbon cannot be more saturated with hydrogen than C_nH_{2n+2}, e.g. C_3H_9 is impossible.

- The molecular ion may *not* be formed for many reasons, but a common oddity of simple spectra is that a hydrogen atom may be lost from an electronegative atom to which it is attached. Thus for simple alcohols the peak at $M - 1$ is often more important than the molecular ion peak. (See the mass spectrum of ethanol in *Structure, Bonding and the Periodic Table*, p.8.)

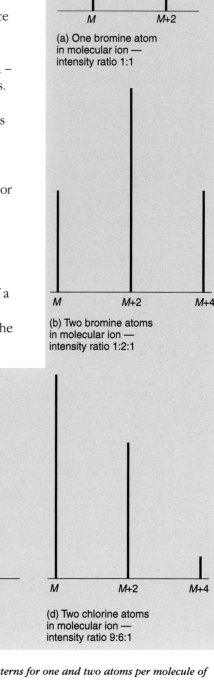

(a) One bromine atom in molecular ion — intensity ratio 1:1

(b) Two bromine atoms in molecular ion — intensity ratio 1:2:1

(c) One chlorine atom in molecular ion — intensity ratio 3:1

(d) Two chlorine atoms in molecular ion — intensity ratio 9:6:1

Figure 4.13 Molecular ion patterns for one and two atoms per molecule of bromine or chlorine

ORGANIC ANALYSIS AND STRUCTURE DETERMINATION

Two examples

A hydrocarbon X

The deduction of the structure of simple alkanes is rather difficult, since there is no heteroatom such as O or Cl that can be associated with fragmentary masses. The exercise is somewhat academic, however, since they have been extensively investigated by the petroleum companies and the mass spectrum is more likely to be used for identification by matching than for peak-by-peak interpretation. The spectrum in Figure 4.14 is that of the saturated hydrocarbon **X**.

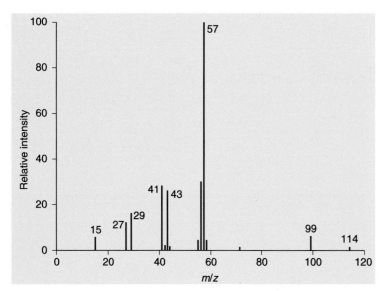

Figure 4.14 Mass spectrum of the unknown alkane X

The molecular ion is just detectable at $M = 114$: the hydrocarbon **X** is one of the 18 isomeric octanes, C_8H_{18} – unless of course the molecular ion has been missed! So weak a peak suggests that the ion can break down very easily into stable tertiary or secondary carbocations, and it is likely to be a branched structure. The peak at $m = 15$ is unusually strong, which suggests several terminal CH_3— groups: again an indication of much branching.

The base peak at $m = 57$ suggests a very stable C_4H_9— unit; this is almost certainly tertiary. This idea is supported by the absence of peaks corresponding to C_5 or C_6, which would be expected from a long-chain octane. The peak corresponding to C_7 ($m = 99$) could occur from a structure containing the —$C(CH_3)_3$ group by loss of one of the three methyl radicals (during fragmentation) from this end of the molecule to give three (identical) C_7 secondary carbocations.

If one end of the molecule is a tertiary butyl group, then the number of isomers is reduced to four (**A–D**):

$(CH_3)_3C — CH_2CH_2CH_2CH_3$

A

$(CH_3)_3C — CH_2CH(CH_3)_2$

B

$(CH_3)_3C — CHCH_2CH_3$
        |
       CH_3

C

$(CH_3)_3C — C(CH_3)_3$

D

- **A** is unlikely since fission of the long chain might give rise to some C_5 and C_6 fragments. It is not safe to say that they would also give weaker C_2 and C_3 fragments, since these might come from other, secondary fragmentations.

- **B** would form C_3 or C_7 secondary carbocations, and is thus a possibility.

- **C** would give a very strong base peak, since intensity of the peak at $m = 57$ from the tertiary butyl group would be increased by secondary butyl ions of the same mass. However, fragmentation at the other side of the single methyl side-chain would give a secondary C_6 fragment, which is not apparent. This suggests that C is not the isomer.

- **D** would give a very strong base peak with either of two tertiary butyl ions possible and easy formation of a C_7 fragment, but further fragmentation is difficult to predict.

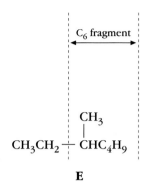

E

Had the original assumption, that the highest level of branching was tertiary, been wrong, e.g. the structure was of the form **E**, then the presence of C_6 fragments would have been inescapable.

Thus the most likely structures for **X** are **B** and **D**, and it is not safe to choose between them (without known spectra for comparison). Either the use of NMR or the synthesis of the two compounds and comparisons of their mass spectra (or IR spectra) would be required.

A compound Y of C, H, O and Cl

The formula of **Y** may be known to be $C_{13}H_9OCl$ ($M_r = 216.0342$) because high-resolution mass spectrometry gave a value of 216.03 or it may have been analysed by more conventional combustion analysis.

The main peaks, after removal of the ^{13}C isotope peaks and minor peaks caused by loss of H• or H_2, are listed in Table 4.4.

The molecular ion region (Figure 4.15) is instructive since it shows that (i) $M_r = 216$ and (ii) the molecule contains one chlorine atom since the peaks at $m = 216$ and 218 are in the ratio 3:1. The minor peaks at $m = 217$ and 219 are mainly the result of ^{13}C, which is becoming important with this number of carbon atoms.

Table 4.4 *Peaks in the mass spectrum of the unknown compound Y*

M	Intensity
51	22
77	50
105	100
111	30
113	10
139	75
141	25
181	10
216	30
218	10

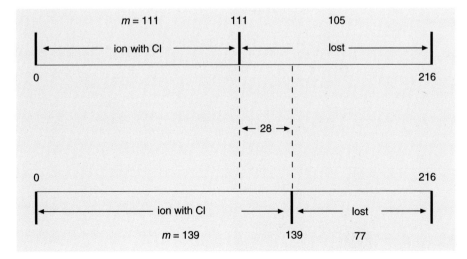

Figure 4.16 Determining relationships between peaks

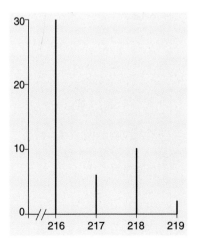

Figure 4.15 Molecular ion region of the mass spectrum of the unknown compound Y

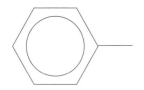

C_6H_5—
m = 77

Fragments at m = 111 and 139 retain one ^{35}Cl atom (Figure 4.16). They differ from 216 by 105 and 77, respectively, and these fragments (if they can separately form positive ions) may well give rise to the observed peaks at these masses. m = 77 is very characteristic of a phenyl group and this is likely to be (i) the species responsible for the peak at this value and (ii) the ion fragment split from the molecular ion to give the ion of mass 139.

The two chlorine-containing fragments differ by 28 as do the two non-chlorine-containing fragments, which indicates that the chlorine-containing group (m = 111) is joined to the phenyl group (m = 77) by a bridge of mass m = 28. Immediate possibilities are —N═N—, —CO— and —CH_2CH_2—. If the compound contains no nitrogen, —N═N— is ruled out; and if oxygen is known to be present —CO— is the only possibility. The IR spectrum would clearly show a C═O group but, taken in isolation, it may not show it to be a bridge. The smaller chlorine-containing fragment at m = 111 must contain a group of mass 111 – 35 = 76, and if we replace the Cl by H for ease of recognition the group will have mass 77. This is likely to be a phenyl group – but not the one already identified since that could not have contained a chloro-substituent. The molecule **Y**, if known to contain one oxygen atom, must therefore be bridged by the —CO— group and have one of the structures **A**–**C**:

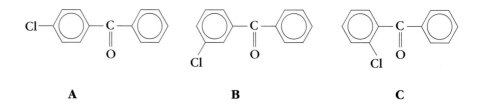

A

B

C

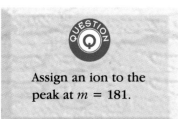

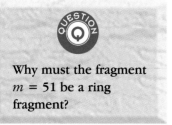

The fragment at m = 181 is not helpful and that at 51 is presumably a ring fragment, e.g. C_4H_3. The mass spectrum does not allow distinction between these three isomers but would certainly have distinguished between, say, **D** and **E**:

D

E

QUESTION

Assign an ion to the peak at m = 181.

QUESTION

Why must the fragment m = 51 be a ring fragment?

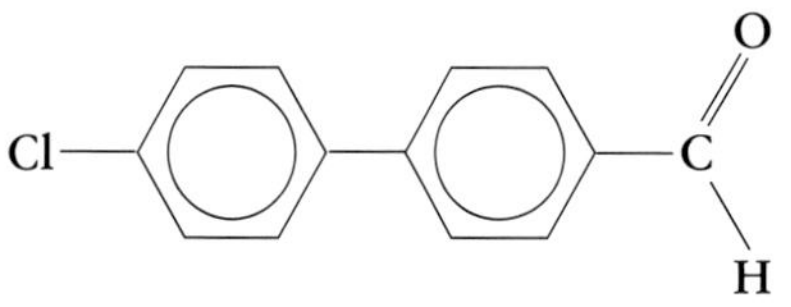

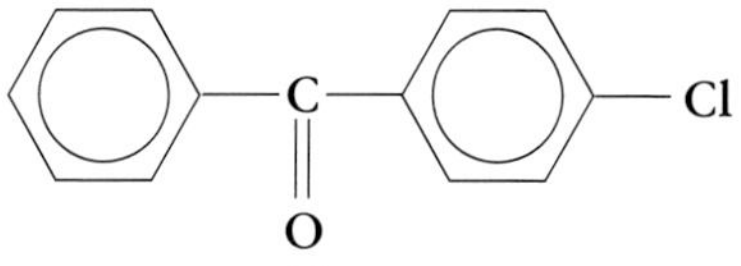

5 Phase equilibrium

Vapour pressure

When a pure liquid (or solid) is placed in a vacuum at a given temperature, an equilibrium is set up between the particles in the liquid and the vapour particles above it. The pressure of the vapour reaches an equilibrium value called the **saturated vapour pressure** (SVP): this is commonly referred to more loosely as the 'vapour pressure'.

For a given temperature, the pressure of vapour is constant; and the more volatile the liquid (the lower its boiling point), the higher is the equilibrium pressure. Thus, at 25°C, the SVP of water (b.p. 100°C) is 2260 Pa but that of the more volatile benzene (b.p. 80°C) is 9980 Pa.

The pressure of the vapour is largely unaffected by the presence of other gases (e.g. air), provided that they do not dissolve to a large extent in the liquid considered. The pressure of the vapour is affected, however, by solutes dissolved in, or miscible with, the liquid. Thus the SVP of sea water is less than 2260 Pa at 25°C because the dissolved salts lower the SVP of the water in it.

Figure 5.1 François Raoult (1830–1901)

Binary mixtures

Raoult's law

A situation of particular interest to the organic chemist is the vapour pressure and behaviour on heating of mixtures of organic liquids. The situation was investigated in the nineteenth century by Raoult (Figure 5.1), who found that, for many liquid mixtures, each component appeared to have its own vapour pressure. This was proportional both to the mole fraction of the component and to the vapour pressure it would have if pure.

Raoult's law can be expressed mathematically as

$$p_A = \left(\tfrac{n_A}{N}\right) \times p_A^{\circ}$$

where p_A is the equilibrium vapour pressure of liquid **A** in a liquid mixture, p_A° is the SVP of pure liquid **A** at that temperature, n_A is the number of moles of **A** in the mixture, and N is the total number of moles of all the liquids in the mixture.

Mixtures that obey Raoult's law exactly are said to be **ideal**.

Graphical representation of Raoult's law

A mixture containing two components, e.g. octane and hexane, is called a **binary mixture**. A simple graph can be drawn, for *any one temperature*, to show the relationship between vapour pressure and composition for an *ideal* binary mixture. The composition of the mixture is expressed in an unusual way, as

Raoult's law
The vapour pressure of any component of a liquid mixture is the product of the mole fraction of that component and its vapour pressure when pure at that temperature.

Example
If 1 mol of benzene and 1 mol of methylbenzene were mixed at 25°C, the mole fraction of benzene would be $\tfrac{1}{2}$, and the vapour pressure of benzene (in that mixture) would be half the value for pure benzene, i.e. 9980/2 = 4990 Pa.

mole fraction. Thus the x-axis has a limited range: from 0 to 1 (increasing left to right) for one component, mirrored by 1 to 0 (increasing right to left) for the other, as shown in Figure 5.2.

Ideal liquids obey Raoult's law, and the vapour pressure of each component is represented by a line from 0, for none of that component, to p° for pure component, i.e. a mole fraction of 1 (Figure 5.2). In reality, the graph is seldom linear because liquids are seldom ideal, but for many similar liquids the departures from ideality are small.

Figure 5.2 Vapour pressure–composition behaviour of an ideal binary liquid mixture: octane plus hexane at T = 298 K

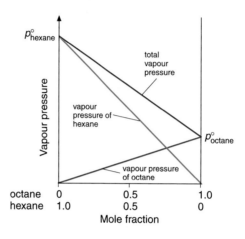

Departures from Raoult's law

Imagine a simple pure liquid, **A**, at a given temperature. The forces of attraction between its particles, separated as they are by a more-or-less fixed distance, will not vary much from one particle to another. It is this force of attraction, the **intermolecular bonding**, that tends to hold the particles in the liquid state. The greater this force, the less volatile is the liquid, the lower is its vapour pressure at a given temperature and the higher is its boiling point at a given pressure.

Now imagine that a second liquid, **B**, is mixed with the first. We begin by assuming that the force of attraction between molecules of **A** and molecules of **B** is the same as the force of attraction of **A** with **A** and of **B** with **B**. Then the probability of molecules of **A** escaping from the liquid (vaporising) will only be affected by the fact that there are fewer molecules of **A**, i.e. a lower mole fraction of **A**, and **A** will behave ideally.

The more nearly two liquids resemble one another in molecular structure and composition (e.g. pentane and hexane; methanol and ethanol; benzene and methylbenzene; 1-chlorohexane and 1-chloroheptane), the more likely they are to have similar intermolecular forces of attraction, and the more likely they are to show ideal behaviour.

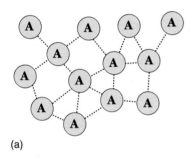

(a)

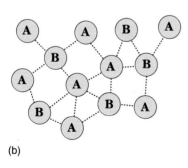

(b)

Figure 5.3 Forces of attraction between molecules of (a) a pure liquid and (b) a mixture of two liquids which resemble each other in molecular structure and composition

As the forces of attraction of the molecules of **A** with **A**, the molecules of **B** with **B**, and the molecules of **A** with **B** become more disparate, so the mixture of **A** and **B** becomes less ideal in its behaviour. If the vapour pressure of the mixture *exceeds* that predicted by Raoult's law, then it is said to show **positive deviation**; and if the vapour pressure is *less than* ideal, this is **negative deviation** (Figure 5.4).

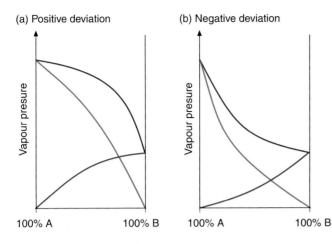

Figure 5.4 (a) Positive and (b) negative deviations from Raoult's law, showing the contributions of components

Remember!
Positive and negative deviations from Raoult's law refer to a greater or smaller *vapour pressure* than ideal. Graphs of boiling point against composition (fixed pressure) look very similar to those for vapour pressure against composition (fixed temperature) but always curve in the opposite sense. You will be meeting them later and it is easy to confuse the two.

Vapour pressure and boiling point

If the temperature of a liquid is increased, it boils when the vapour pressure reaches the applied pressure. Water in the laboratory boils at 100°C at 1 atm pressure; at the top of a mountain, it would boil at a lower temperature. That is an ideal statement, and liquids in practice often fail to boil until the temperature is slightly greater than their 'true' boiling point. The active process of boiling is not a true equilibrium. This is often observed when water and aqueous solutions are boiled, if there is no dissolved air to form a nucleus for the bubbles. You may have noted a disconcerting tendency of distilled water and laboratory solutions to 'bump' when you try to boil them. Their temperatures rise locally above their 'true' boiling points, and then they boil explosively at these locations. Another common example is the noisy way in which re-heated water boils when it has previously been boiled in an electric kettle with the expulsion of its dissolved air. The bubbles of steam form with greater difficulty and at a slightly higher temperature.

As we have seen, the vapour pressure of liquid mixtures depends not only on the temperature but also on the composition; hence composition affects the boiling point. A graph of boiling point against composition at a given pressure looks like the graph of (total) vapour pressure against composition at a fixed temperature if the latter were 'rotated' by 180° about a horizontal line (Figure 5.5).

Of course, the positions on the axes will depend on the scales chosen; you should not expect an exact rotation. In an ideal example, the straight line of the vapour pressure (v.p.) diagram becomes slightly curved in the boiling point (b.p.) graph. The relationship between the two is shown in the 'three-dimensional' graph in Figure 5.6; it is intended to help you to understand – do not try to learn it!

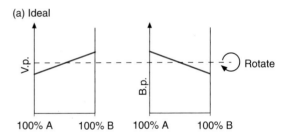

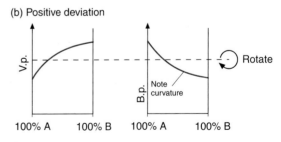

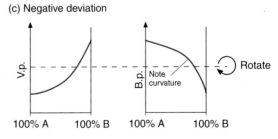

Figure 5.5 (a) Ideal behaviour, (b) positive and (c) negative deviations from Raoult's law accompanied by the boiling point graphs of the same mixtures

PHASE EQUILIBRIUM

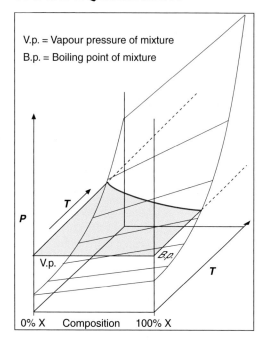

V.p. = Vapour pressure of mixture

B.p. = Boiling point of mixture

Figure 5.6 B.p. and v.p. curves

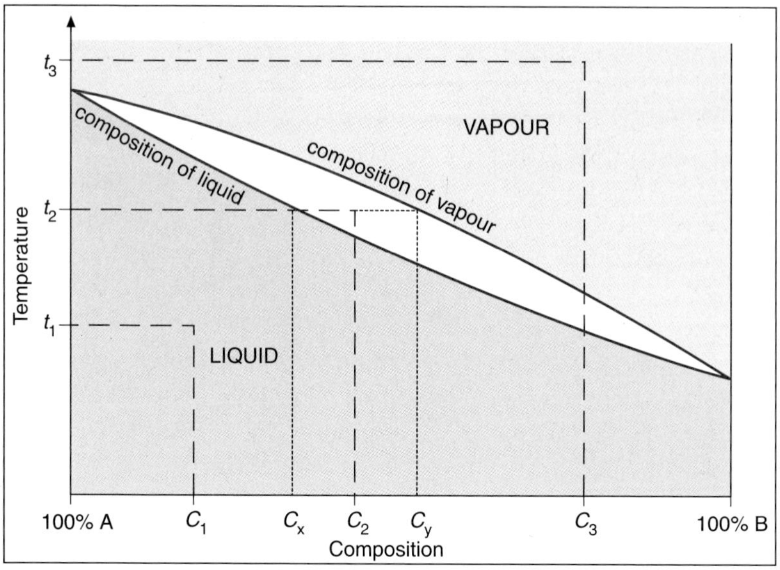

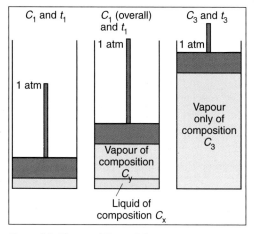

Figure 5.8 Phases of Figure 5.6

Figure 5.9 A laboratory fractional distillation apparatus

Figure 5.7 A phase diagram showing the composition of liquid and vapour in an ideal binary mixture

Composition of the vapour

So far we have considered how the vapour pressure (fixed temperature) and boiling point (fixed pressure) of a mixture vary with composition. We have not considered the vapour produced. Clearly, if a *pure liquid* is boiled, the vapour is pure – the question of composition does not arise. If a *mixture* is boiled, the vapour is unlikely to have the same composition. Even though the liquid mixture shows ideal behaviour, it will usually be true that the vapour in equilibrium with the liquid is richer in the more volatile component (but see azeotrope formation below).

We can extend our boiling point graph to show this difference in composition of the vapour in equilibrium with the liquid (Figure 5.7). Such a diagram is called a **phase diagram**, because if we had a mixture of **A** and **B**, of known composition at a known temperature, alone (no air present) in a closed container, we could say exactly what form the contents would take (Figure 5.8).

Fractional distillation

Organic chemists usually separate mixtures of liquids by the process of fractional distillation. This involves the use of a fractionating column. A typical laboratory apparatus is shown in Figure 5.9, but the design and complexity of distillation (fractionating) columns varies greatly. Those for the fractionation of liquid air separate the components, but this low-temperature distillation is usually carried out in two stages under different pressures. Petroleum has many components: the commercial distillation simply vaporizes all that will boil and continuously removes *mixtures*, 'fractions' with a range of boiling points from various condensation trays at different heights of the column.

It is tempting to suppose that, if we boil a mixture of liquids, they will leave the mixture as the temperature rises, one at a time, in order of increasing boiling point. Such is not the case. It may be possible to separate all of them by **fractional distillation**, but not because they leave the liquid in this simple order.

Suppose that we tried to separate an ideal binary liquid mixture in a sequence of simple distillations. Suppose that we boil a great deal of the mixture of composition c_1 (Figure 5.10). It will boil at temperature t_1 and the vapour in equilibrium has the composition c_2 (richer in the more volatile **B**). Of course, we cannot boil off much vapour before affecting the composition of the liquid, which must be getting richer in the less volatile **A**; and if we do affect the liquid composition, that in turn will affect the vapour. We condense *all* of the small amount of vapour – that way its composition cannot change because it is not in equilibrium – and we have a very small amount of distillate of unchanged composition c_2 (Figure 5.10).

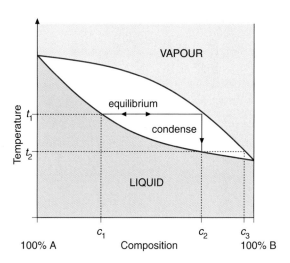

Figure 5.10 Phase diagram for the separation of an ideal binary mixture

We then boil the small amount of liquid of composition c_2 (in fresh apparatus). It boils at temperature t_2 and the vapour in equilibrium will have composition c_3. But, of course, we can only take a minute amount of the vapour this time without affecting the composition of the liquid, and if we distilled all of the liquid we would achieve no purification whatsoever! Finally, by repetition of the process, as can be seen from Figure 5.10, we should be able to get a pathetically small amount of (essentially) pure **B**.

Such a stepped diagram shows that the separation of **B** from **A** is theoretically possible, and it can be used by chemists to estimate the difficulty of separation of a particular mixture (the more 'steps' the harder it will be). It is also used to estimate the efficiency of distillation columns based on the number of 'steps' achieved in one distillation using the equipment under test.

It is not very satisfactory to explain fractional distillation in this simple and pedestrian way, but it does illustrate that the process is possible.

The operation of a fractionating column involves a temperature gradient up the column and a corresponding concentration or composition gradient (Figure 5.11). At any moment of time, an infinite number of equilibria between vapour and liquid exist in the column.

As soon as the liquid in the flask boils and gives off vapour richer in **B**, the liquid becomes richer in **A** and its boiling point rises. Further vapour that leaves the liquid does so at a progressively higher temperature and, although the vapour will always be richer in **B** than the liquid in equilibrium, the percentage of **B** in both is

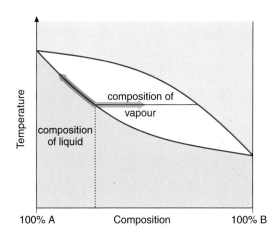

Figure 5.11 Phase diagram for an ideal binary mixture showing the direction of continuous change in composition of liquid and vapour

PHASE EQUILIBRIUM

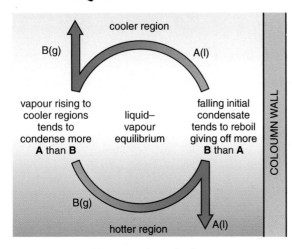

Figure 5.12 Equilibrium at the wall of a fractionating column

continually falling. The first vapour condenses, thereby heating the column, and runs back down the column to be reboiled. Gradually the column develops a temperature gradient and continuously brings descending condensate into equilibrium with rising vapour (Figure 5.12).

An efficient column is either long enough or sufficiently sophisticated in its design to bring about the necessary equilibration between evaporate and condensate, so that, in operation, the top of the column is approximately at the boiling point of the more volatile component (**B**) and this distils.

Large departures from Raoult's law

Provided that the vapour pressure of a binary mixture is always between those of its pure components, and they have different vapour pressures, the mixture can be separated by fractional distillation (Figure 5.13).

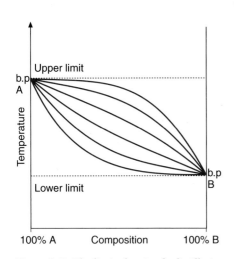

Figure 5.13 The limits for simple distillation

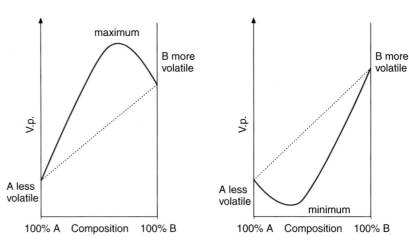

Figure 5.14 Graphs showing the formation of maximum and minimum vapour pressures

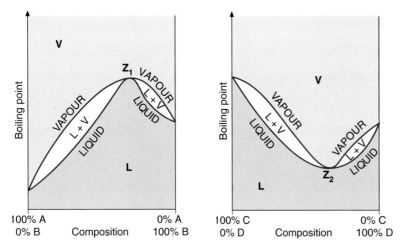

Figure 5.15 Phase diagrams showing maximum and minimum boiling points:
(a) mixture with maximum boiling point; (b) mixture with minimum boiling point

However, if positive deviation takes the vapour pressure of the mixture above that of the more volatile component, or if negative deviation takes the vapour pressure below that of the less volatile component, a maximum or a minimum will be produced in the curve (Figure 5.14). When this happens, then, at best, only some of one of the two components can be separated in a pure condition by fractional distillation.

When a maximum or minimum is present in the phase diagram, i.e. a maximum or minimum boiling point is shown, then the 'two-phase' or 'liquid + vapour' area between the liquid and vapour curves is divided on either side of the maximum or minimum (Figure 5.15).

As we have seen on, the result of distillation of an ideal mixture can be predicted by drawing a series of steps from the initial composition and liquid boiling point 'down' the (white) liquid + vapour area. The result of distillation of non-ideal binary mixtures is predicted similarly (Figure 5.15).

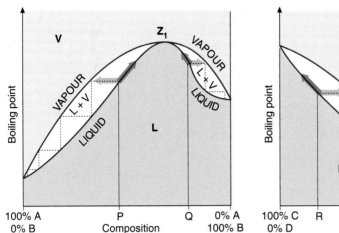
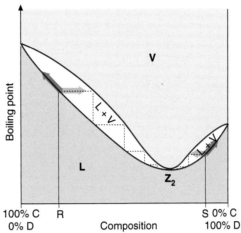

Figure 5.16 Phase diagrams showing 'steps' and directions of change: (a) mixture with maximum boiling point; (b) mixture with minimum boiling point

In each case, the composition of the vapour will move in the direction of the horizontal arrow towards the final composition of the distillate, and the composition of the remaining liquid (of ever-increasing boiling point) will move in the direction of the sloping arrow.

For maximum-boiling-point mixtures, it can be seen that **A** will distil from a mixture of composition **P** (Figure 5.16a), but **B** will distil from a mixture of composition **Q**. For either initial composition, the liquid left in the flask will increase in boiling point until it reaches the maximum, and then mixture Z_1 will distil unchanged.

In contrast, from the minimum-boiling-point mixture (Figure 5.16b), the mixture Z_2 will distil from liquids of composition **R** or **S** until the excess **C** or **D** is left in the flask. This will finally distil unchanged.

The mixtures, **Z**, are called **azeotropes**. Although they distil unchanged, they are not compounds, since their composition is dependent on the pressure.

Aqueous solutions of acids not infrequently show negative deviation, with maximum-boiling-point azeotropes (Table 5.1).

Table 5.1 *Some maximum-boiling azeotropes*

Acid	Percentage by mass in mixture/%	Mole fraction of acid	Boiling point of azeotrope/°C	Boiling point of pure acid/°C
HF	35.6	0.34	111	19
HCl	20.2	0.11	109	−85
HBr	47.5	0.17	126	−76
HI	57.0	0.16	127	−34
HNO_3	67.4	0.37	121	86
HCOOH	77.4	0.57	107	101

Negative deviation is less common among organic compounds, where positive deviation leading to minimum-boiling-point azeotropes is more common.

The best-known example of this kind is that of ethanol and water, though the minimum is only just present! The boiling point of pure ethanol is 78.32°C and that of the minimum-boiling-point azeotrope is 78.17°C. When fermented carbohydrate solutions are distilled, the highest possible concentration of ethanol in the distillate is 96% (mole fraction 0.903). This is of little relevance to manufacturers of alcoholic drinks, since even the strongest spirits are only about 40% ethanol.

For chemists who require pure anhydrous ethanol, the small amount of residual water must be removed, e.g. chemically by the addition of calcium oxide:

$$CaO \quad + \quad H_2O \quad \rightarrow \quad Ca(OH)_2$$

Some examples of pairs of liquids, **A** and **B**, which show a more obvious positive deviation from Raoult's law and form minimum-boiling-point azeotropes are given in Table 5.2.

Table 5.2 *Some minimum-boiling azeotropes*

Liquid A	B.p. of A/°C	Liquid B	B.p. of B/°C	B.p. of azeotrope/°C	Percentage of A in azeotrope/%
$CHCl_3$	61	hexane	69	60	83
CCl_4	77	ethanol	78	65	86
$SiCl_4$	57	nitromethane	101	54	94
ethane-1, 2-diol	197	2-nitromethylbenzene	222	188	48
methyl ethanoate	57	cyclopentane	49	43	38

We can summarise the behaviour of binary mixtures on distillation as shown in Table 5.3. Note that if two liquids form an azeotrope, assuming that they are not mixed in the exact azeotropic proportions, it might be possible to get some of *one* of the liquids from the mixture by distillation, but *not all* of that liquid and *not both* of the liquids.

Table 5.3 *Summary of the behaviour of binary mixtures on distillation*

Phase diagram	Distillate	Left behind
Ideal (nearly)	More volatile component	Less volatile component
Minimum-boiling-point azeotrope	Azeotrope	One* pure component
Maximum-boiling-point azeotrope	One* pure component	Azeotrope
* The component present in excess of the azeotropic composition		

Appendix: Nuclear magnetic resonance spectroscopy

NMR is not part of the current London Examinations syllabus, but is shortly to be introduced. Its importance in modern organic structure determination cannot be overstated. For the benefit of students who wish to know a little about the basis of NMR, this appendix has been added.

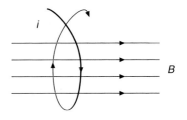

Introduction

An electric current, i, (one or more moving charges), in a coil has an associated magnetic field, B.

An atomic nucleus, which *must* carry an electric charge, *may* also be spinning: if it is, it will have a (very small) associated magnetic field, δB.

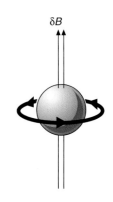

The nucleus of the common isotope of hydrogen (a proton) does spin and behaves as a small magnet. It is perhaps fortunate for the development of this branch of spectroscopy that the common isotopes of carbon and oxygen, ^{12}C and ^{16}O, do not.

In an external magnetic field, B, a spinning nucleus can have two or more energy levels. Again, it is fortunate that the hydrogen nucleus can have only two (Figure A.1): a higher energy level, in which the small magnetic field of the proton is opposed to the external magnetic field, and a lower energy level, in which it is aligned with the external magnetic field. The larger the magnetic field, the larger the difference between these energy levels.

If a proton aligned with a magnetic field is supplied with electromagnetic radiation of the correct frequency to supply the energy difference between the two energy levels, it will absorb radiation and 'flip' to the higher level. This is **nuclear magnetic resonance**.

The magnetic fields have to be very large in order to make measurement of a spectrum feasible. If the field is slightly unstable or non-uniform, the spectrum will lack fine detail. Using fields of the order of 1 T (tesla), resonance of the proton occurs in the microwave region at about 40 MHz. Recent, more powerful spectrometers use superconducting coils cooled in liquid helium.

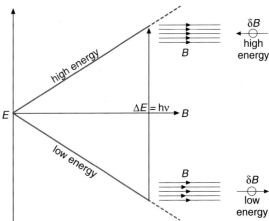

With the development of more and more sophisticated instruments, other nuclei, particularly ^{13}C, have been studied. In consequence, it has become usual to refer to nuclear magnetic resonance studies of the hydrogen nucleus as **proton magnetic resonance** (or ^1H NMR).

Figure A.1 The two energy levels of a hydrogen nucleus in an external magnetic field, B. As the field B increases, so does the resonant frequency ν

Proton magnetic resonance

Within a molecule, local environmental effects alter the magnetic field to which a proton is subjected. The electrons in the bond holding the hydrogen atom to its neighbour interact with, and reduce, the external magnetic field. This **shielding effect** is greater the 'nearer' the bonding electrons are to the proton. They are less effective if they are shared with a strongly electronegative atom such as O in O—H or N in N—H than when shared with carbon. Hence, as the external field rises (for a given radio frequency and hence fixed ΔE), —O—H protons, which are less shielded, would resonate before —C—H protons. The standard against which the magnetic fields at resonance are measured is that for the absorption of the protons in tetramethylsilane (TMS, $(CH_3)_4Si$), which has twelve 'identical' protons in the molecule.

The pure sample for examination is often dissolved in a non-proton-containing solvent such as tetrachloromethane or deuterochloroform ($CDCl_3$). The nucleus of deuterium, ^2H, does not have spin and so does not affect the spectrum. A little TMS is added. Better resolution is obtained if the sample is spun in the field.

Modern spectrometers do not necessarily operate by having a fixed radio-frequency source and a varying magnetic field, or vice versa, but spectra are plotted as if this was the mode of operation.

Methanol contains protons connected to two different atoms, C and O. As the field is increased, first the —OH protons, then the methyl —CH_3 protons and finally the TMS protons resonate in the fixed microwave radiation (Figure A.2).

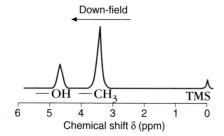

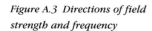

Figure A.2 The NMR spectrum of methanol

Chemical shift

The difference between the resonant field of a given proton and that of the protons in TMS is called the **chemical shift** and is given the symbol, δ. The weaker the field at which proton resonance occurs, the greater is the chemical shift and the more 'down-field' the absorption peak is said to be (see Figure A.2). The absolute value of the chemical shift is proportional to the external field, and so is the total energy difference between the magnetic states of the proton. The shift is thus expressed as parts per million (ppm) of the field for TMS. The peak for TMS is assigned to zero on the chemical shift scale (as in Figure A.2). The energy differences are also proportional to the microwave frequency ($\Delta E = h\nu$); hence this method of defining chemical shift also represents ppm of the oscillating electromagnetic field.

On a spectrum the direction of the field strength (fixed microwave frequency) and the direction of the frequency (fixed magnetic field) run in opposite directions (Figure A.3).

Figure A.3 Directions of field strength and frequency

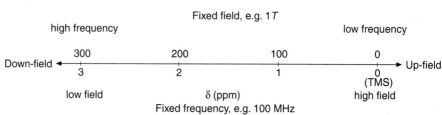

If all that NMR could do was indicate that a proportion of the hydrogen atoms was bonded to O or N rather than to C in an organic compound, it would be less useful than IR. However, the shielding effect does not require a heteroatom to show itself. Protons on a carbon atom adjacent to an electron-attracting group will be **deshielded** and will be more vulnerable to the external magnetic field. They will thus resonate at a lower external field and the absorption peak will move 'down-field'. One advantage of TMS as a standard is that the silicon atom is less electronegative than carbon, a rare situation in organic compounds, and the increased shielding effect on the protons of the methyl groups pushes the absorption peak well 'up-field' and outside the range of all common absorptions.

Chemical shifts are tabulated for all groups adjacent to protons in CH, CH_2 or CH_3 and, since the *area* of the absorption peak gives a measure of the number of protons in this particular environment, the spectrum can give a far more reliable picture of a molecule than IR, but requires considerable thought in its interpretation.

Table A.1 shows some approximate values of chemical shifts for protons in CH_3X, where X represents a halogen. Note that, as the electronegativity of the halogen increases, so does the chemical shift. Similarly, the chemical shifts for protons in —CH_2— and >CH— are progressively greater than those for CH_3—, i.e. the corresponding absorption is found 'down-field'.

Tables of these shifts are widely published, but need treating with caution because all except terminal methyl groups have at least two groups attached, and chemical shifts cannot simply be added together.

Table A.1 *Chemical shifts caused by halogens on methyl protons*

Halogen	Cl	Br	I
Shift δ	3.0	2.7	2.2

Spin coupling

So far we have looked at one proton in a magnetic field and considered how the external field is altered in the region of the proton by the shielding effect of the immediate bonding electrons. Nearby protons may further modify the absorption by interacting with the proton under consideration. A spinning proton influences the spin of electrons in adjacent bonds, which, in turn, influence the spin (and associated minute magnetic field) of other protons.

We shall take it as a simplifying rule that this effect is important only when protons are attached to *adjacent* (carbon) atoms. Two protons bonded to adjacent carbon atoms in different environments might each be expected to give rise to one peak, resulting in a spectrum with two peaks. In fact, they often give rise to four such peaks (Figure A.4), assuming that the machine can resolve them. Each proton can react to the external field in one of two ways depending on how it has been affected by the presence of the other proton.

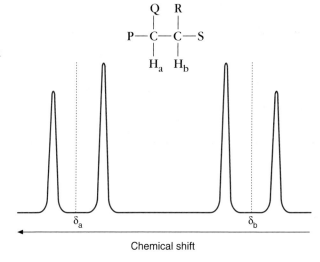

Figure A.4 Each proton splits the peak of the other

Thus the two peaks become doublets, i.e. they are split. This effect is called **proton spin coupling**. The two peaks of the doublet are not of equal intensity unless there is a big difference in their chemical shifts. As the two proton chemical shifts become nearer, one peak of each doublet gradually dominates until, in the extreme case of two protons on the *same* carbon atom, not only does the smaller peak of each doublet disappear but the protons both resonate at the same field and there is only one peak (of twice the area) for the pair – hence our rule about *adjacent* carbon atoms.

If a proton has n protons on *adjacent* carbon atoms, then 0, 1, ..., n of them can be aligned with it, i.e. there are $n + 1$ possible spin variations corresponding to $n + 1$ slightly different resonant fields. Thus the CH_2 peak (next to CH_3) in bromoethane is split into four tiny peaks, whereas the CH_3 peak, despite having more protons, is split into only three by the adjacent CH_2 protons. The fact that there are two (CH_2) and three (CH_3) protons, respectively, is revealed by the *area* of the peaks, not by their shapes. Modern NMR machines integrate the curves and display the areas of the peaks as well as their position and shape (Figure A.5).

It can thus be seen that many simple problems can be solved by inspection of the spectrum without a precise knowledge of δ. Provided that the chemical shift was sufficient to separate all the absorption peaks, we might expect to

Table A.1 *Distinguishing the four isomers CH_3CClCH_3 by NMR*

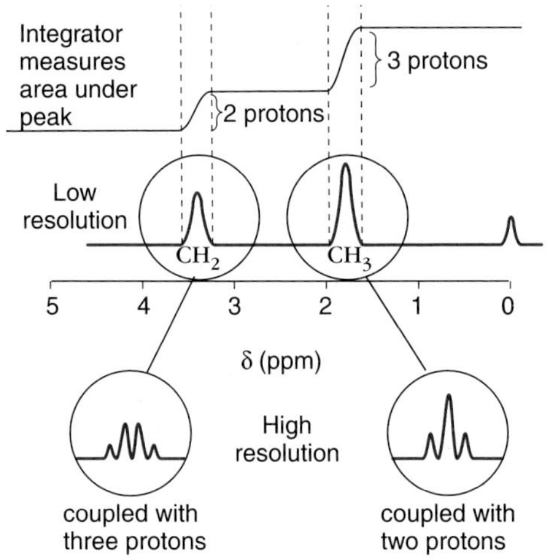

Figure A.5 Schematic NMR spectrum of bromoethane (CH_3CH_2Br)

Isomer	$CH_3CH_2CHCl_2$			$CH_3CCl_2CH_3$		
Unit	CH_3	CH_2	$CHCl_2$	CH_3	CCl_2	CH_3
Peak type*	3	5	3	1	0	1
Area of peak	3	2	1	→	0	→6
Total number of peaks	3			1		
Isomer	$CH_3CHClCH_2Cl$			$ClCH_2CH_2CH_2Cl$		
Unit	CH_3	$CHCl$	CH_2Cl	$ClCH_2$	CH_2	CH_2Cl
Peak type*	2	6	2	3	5	3
Area of peak	3	1	2	→	2	→4
Total number of peaks	3			2		

*Peak type: 1 = singlet, 2 = doublet, 3 = triplet, etc.

distinguish between the four isomers of $C_3H_6Cl_2$ by inspection of their NMR spectra (Table A.2). Note that the terminal methyl and chloromethyl groups would give rise to only one peak, but, had we considered higher homologues than C_3, the terminal groups might have had different neighbours and would have different chemical shifts.

Protons on adjacent atoms other than carbon may interact in a more complicated way. Thus, in ethanol, the —OH proton may give three peaks (a triplet) or just one peak (a singlet), depending on whether or not it interacts with the CH_2 protons. The CH_2 can give four peaks by interacting with CH_3 alone, or five peaks (a quintuplet) if it interacts with the —OH proton as well. This is very solvent-dependent: if hydrogen-bonding occurs between ethanol molecules (see page 4), the rapid interchange of protons (hydrogen atoms) does not allow spin coupling of the —OH proton with those on the CH_2.

^{13}C NMR, though technically more difficult and also more difficult to interpret, is yielding important information about the carbon skeleton of complicated molecules. NMR spectroscopy is in a state of rapid development.

Examination questions

1 Many insects communicate using chemical compounds called pheromones. Such compounds may be quite simple and the organism is extremely sensitive to their presence. Insect alarm pheromones have been studied as potential insecticides. Using the information which follows, deduce the formula for an alarm pheromone, **P**, in ants.

(a) **P** contains 73.47% carbon and 10.20% hydrogen by mass, the remainder being oxygen. The mass spectrum shows a significant peak at $m/z = 98$, but none higher than this. Find the empirical and molecular formula for **P**. **(5)**

(b) **P** decolorises bromine readily at room temperature. 0.735 g of **P** dissolved in tetrachloromethane reacts with 30.0 cm³ of a 0.250 mol dm⁻³ solution of bromine in the same solvent. Use this information to find the nature and number of functional groups in the molecule. **(3)**

(c) **P** gives a precipitate with 2,4-dinitrophenylhydrazine and reduces ammoniacal silver nitrate solution on warming. What is the second functional group in **P**? Give your reasons. **(2)**

(d) **P** can be reduced by hydrogen/platinum at room temperature or by sodium borohydride in ether. In each case 1 mol of **P** adds on 1 mol of hydrogen but the products are not the same. Explain these observations. **(3)**

(e) The carbon chain in **P** is unbranched and the functional groups are adjacent on the chain. **P** has two stereoisomers. Draw the possible structures of **P**. **(2)**

(f) Only one of the stereoisomers is effective at persuading ants to go elsewhere. Suggest why this is so. **(1)**

Total 16 marks
(ULEAC GCE Chemistry (9081/6084), January 1996)

2 The following is adapted from a textbook of practical chemistry which gives details for the preparation of the azo dye phenylazo-2-naphthol.

Dissolve 2.5 g of phenylamine in a mixture of 8 cm³ of hydrochloric acid and 8 cm³ of water in a small beaker. Place in an ice-bath; ignore any crystals that may appear. When the temperature is between 0°C and 5°C, add drop by drop a solution of 2 g of sodium nitrite dissolved in 10 cm³ of water, not allowing the temperature to rise above 5°C. Addition of the sodium nitrite solution should continue until, after a wait of 3–4 minutes, a drop of the reaction mixture gives an immediate blue coloration with starch-iodide paper.

Prepare a solution of 3.9 g of 2-naphthol in 10% aqueous sodium hydroxide in a 250 cm³ beaker and cool in an ice-bath to below 5°C; add 10–15 g of crushed ice to this solution. Stir the mixture and add the diazonium salt prepared as above very slowly; red crystals of the azo compound will separate. When addition is complete, allow the mixture to stand in ice for 10 minutes and then filter the product, using gentle suction, on a Büchner funnel. Wash with water; the product may be recrystallised from glacial ethanoic acid. It has a melting point of 131°C.

(a) Phenylamine is toxic by inhalation and skin absorption; concentrated hydrochloric acid is corrosive and gives harmful fumes. What specific precautions would you therefore take when doing this experiment? **(2)**

(b) Write the equation for the reaction between phenylamine and hydrochloric acid. **(1)**

(c) (i) Why should the mixture be kept between 0°C and 5°C?

(ii) Is the diazotisation exothermic or endothermic? How do you know?

(iii) Why should you wait before testing with starch-iodide paper for the presence of excess nitrite ions? **(5)**

(d) Give the equation, using structural formulae, for the diazo coupling reaction between benzene diazonium chloride and 2-naphthol. **(2)**

(e) The aqueous solution of the diazo compound prepared as in the first paragraph will, if allowed to warm up, turn from very pale yellow to a turbid orange-red and will evolve nitrogen. Why is this? **(2)**

Total 12 marks

(ULEAC GCE Chemistry (9081/6084), January 1996)

3 Consider the reaction scheme, then answer the questions which follow.

(a) Give the reagents and conditions for steps 1, 2 and 3. **(7)**

(b) (i) Write an equation for the reaction of compound **D** with dilute aqueous sodium hydroxide.

(ii) What type of reaction is this? **(2)**

(c) Outline briefly how you would isolate a sample of the aromatic product of the reaction in (b)(i). **(3)**

(d) Give the mechanism for the conversion of **A** to **B**. **(4)**

Total 16 marks

(ULEAC GCE Chemistry (9081/9082/6084), June 1996)

4 (*a*) (i) Give the equation for the reaction of propene with bromine and name the product.

   (ii) Give the mechanism for this reaction. **(5)**

(*b*) (i) Give the reagent and conditions you would use to convert the product of (a)(i) into $CH_3CH(OH)CH_2OH$.

   (ii) What reagent would you use to convert propene directly into $CH_3CH(OH)CH_2OH$?

   (iii) A similar type of compound, $HOCH_2(CHOH)_4CH_2OH$, is used as the basis for sugar-free mints. Explain, from your knowledge of the groups present, why this compound is not retained in fatty tissue but readily finds its way into the urine. **(5)**

(*c*) Propane-1,2-diol, $CH_3CHOHCH_2OH$, can be used to manufacture a polymer.

   (i) Give the structure of a suitable compound which could react with propane-1,2-diol to form a polymer.

   (ii) Give the repeat unit of the polymer formed and name the type of linkage formed between the molecules.

   (iii) This polymer is not considered to be particularly hazardous to the environment. Comment on possible reasons for this. **(5)**

Total 15 marks

(ULEAC GCE Chemistry (9081/9082/6084), June 1996)

5 Outline how the following conversions could be carried out in the laboratory, giving reagents, conditions and equations.

(*a*) (i) $C_6H_5CH_3$ to $C_6H_5CH_2Cl$.

   (ii) Sketch the apparatus you might use to carry out this reaction.

   (iii) Given that the boiling points of $C_6H_5CH_3$ and $C_6H_5CH_2Cl$ are 111°C and 179°C respectively, how would you isolate a pure sample of $C_6H_5CH_2Cl$? **(8)**

(*b*) CH_3CH_2Br to $CH_3CH_2CH_2NH_2$ in two stages. **(7)**

Total 15 marks

(ULEAC GCE Chemistry (9081/9082/6084), June 1996)

6 The sketch below shows the variation in boiling point (at constant pressure) for liquid mixtures of benzene (boiling point 80.1°C) and ethanol (boiling point 78.5°C).

(*a*) (i) Which of the liquids is X?

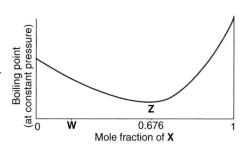
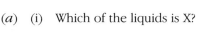

(ii) Copy the sketch above. On your copy draw the curve which represents the variation in composition of the vapour above these liquid mixtures.

(iii) What is represented by the point **Z**?

(iv) Give the mole fraction of benzene in the vapour state at point Z. **(4)**

(b) Identify, by marking your diagram with the letter **Y**, the composition of the vapour given off initially when a liquid mixture of composition **W** is boiled. **(1)**

(c) If the mixture **W** is fractionally distilled, identify

(i) the distillate,

(ii) the liquid remaining in the flask. **(2)**

(d) (i) Draw a sketch to show how the vapour pressure of mixtures of benzene and ethanol varies with concentration, at constant temperature.

(ii) On your sketch draw the line which would have represented the variation in vapour pressure if mixtures of benzene and ethanol behaved ideally (label the line **I**).

(iii) Explain in molecular terms why the mixture of benzene and ethanol does not behave ideally. **(7)**

Total 14 marks
(ULEAC GCE Chemistry (9081/9082/6084), June 1996)

7 (a) (i) State Raoult's law for an ideal mixture of two liquids. **(2)**

(ii) Benzene and methylbenzene may be separated by distillation. Sketch the general form of the boiling point/composition diagram for such a mixture and use it to explain the basis on which fractional distillation rests. **(6)**

(iii) The first stage in the refining of crude oil (petroleum) is fractional distillation. State TWO ways in which the commercial fractional distillation of crude oil differs from the fractional distillation of a simple ideal mixture of two liquids. **(2)**

(b) (i) All lighter (more volatile) fractions from petroleum distillation are useful as fuels. Suggest TWO reasons why the liquid fractions with eight to twelve carbon atoms per molecule are used as motor fuels, rather than the gaseous ones containing from one to four carbon atoms. **(2)**

    (ii) Benzene is added to unleaded petrol to compensate for the absence of tetraethyl lead. Both compounds are hazardous; which hazard is associated with benzene? **(1)**

   (iii) Tetraethyl lead or benzene are added to petrol to prevent pre-ignition. What is pre-ignition and why is it a problem? **(2)**

   (iv) Suggest TWO reasons why unleaded fuel has been promoted by government and the petroleum industry. **(2)**

Total 17 marks
(ULEAC GCE Chemistry (9081/9082/6084), January 1997)

8 Consider the compound **A** which is related to the hormone adrenaline.

  (*a*) Draw the structures of the organic product(s) which you would expect from the reaction of **A** with

    (i)   phosphorus pentachloride, **(1)**

    (ii) dilute hydrochloric acid, **(1)**

   (iii) ethanoyl chloride, **(2)**

   (iv) hot alkaline potassium manganate(VII). **(1)**

  (*b*) Suppose that you have to purify a sample of **A** by recrystallisation from trichloromethane. This solvent is toxic by inhalation and skin absorption but is not flammable.

    (i)   What safety precautions would you take when using this solvent? **(2)**

    (ii) Describe in detail how you would recrystallise a sample of about 5 g of **A**. **(5)**

   (iii) What simple test would you use to determine the purity of your recrystallised material? **(2)**

Total 14 marks
(ULEAC GCE Chemistry (9081/9082/6084), January 1997)

9 (*a*) Polymers may be naturally occurring or synthetic. Name

    (i)   a synthetic polyalkene, **(1)**

    (ii) a synthetic polyamide, **(1)**

   (iii) a natural polyamide, **(1)**

   (iv) a synthetic polymer containing no hydrogen. **(1)**

  (*b*) Terylene is a polymer made from ethane-1,2-diol and benzene-1,4-dicarboxylic acid. It is a condensation polymer.

    (i)   Draw the structural formulae of TWO compounds which are used to make terylene. **(2)**

    (ii) Give a structural formula for the polymer. **(2)**

    (iii) Explain the meaning of the term condensation in this context. **(1)**

    (iv) Suggest why polyesters are not suitable for use under strongly alkaline conditions. **(1)**

(c)   Suggest why polymers such as terylene soften over a range of temperatures rather than having a sharp melting point. **(1)**

Total 11 marks

(ULEAC GCE Chemistry (9081/9082/6084), January 1997)

10 (a)   Give the structural formulae of the THREE structural isomers of C_4H_8 which are non-cyclic. **(3)**

(b)   One of these isomers shows a type of stereoisomerism.

    (i)   Give the structures of the stereoisomers and name them. **(2)**

    (ii) Suggest how these stereoisomers might be distinguished. **(1)**

(c)   One of the isomers of C_4H_8 in (a) reacts with HBr to give two different products, the major of which is a chiral molecule.

    (i)   Identify this isomer of C_4H_8. **(1)**

    (ii) Give the mechanism for the reaction of this isomer with HBr. **(3)**

    (iii) Why is the major product chiral but the minor one not so? **(1)**

    (iv) Why is the chiral product the major one and the non-chiral product the minor one? **(1)**

    (v) The major product of this addition reaction is found to be optically inactive. Explain why this is so. **(2)**

Total 14 marks

(LE GCE Chemistry (6084), June 1997)

11 This question relates to the following reaction scheme.

$$C_2H_5Br \xrightarrow{\text{step 1}} C_2H_5CN \xrightarrow{\text{step 2}} C_2H_5CH_2NH_2 \xrightarrow{\text{step 3}} C_2H_5CH_2OH$$

(a)   Give the reagents and the conditions required for steps 1 and 2. **(6)**

(b)   (i)   Give the mechanism for step 1. **(3)**

    (ii) What type of mechanism is this? **(1)**

(c) The conversion of C_2H_5Br to $C_2H_5CH_2OH$ by this method is ineffective, not least because step 3 gives a very poor yield of only 7%. Outline an alternative synthetic route, stating clearly the reagents and conditions of the steps you suggest. **(6)**

Total 16 marks

(LE GCE Chemistry (6084), June 1997)

Questions 12 and 13 are taken from the 1997 practical examinations. Candidates were expected to find the preliminary information given here in each question. A table of infra-red absorption frequencies was provided in the examination, but the student should use Table 4.1 on page 69 of this book.

12 A compound **Y** produced a yellow precipitate with iodine and aqueous sodium hydroxide and an orange precipitate with 2,4-dinitrophenylhydrazine. It had no effect on ammoniacal silver nitrate.

(a) Infra-red spectrum – substance **Y**

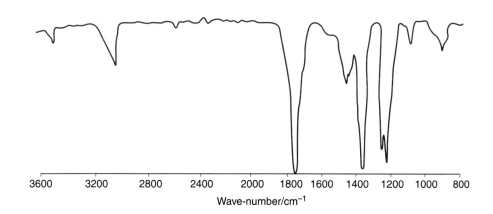

By considering the infra-red spectrum, explain why compound Y may be an aldehyde or a ketone but not a carboxylic acid.

(b) Mass spectrum – substance **Y**

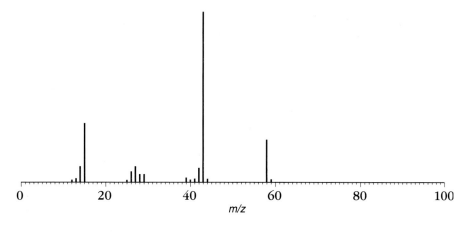

From the mass spectrum, deduce the relative molecular mass of **Y** and suggest a likely structure corresponding to the peak at $m = 43$.

13 A compound **Z** gave a yellow precipitate with iodine and aqueous sodium hydroxide but had no reaction with 2,4-dinitrophenylhydrazine.
The composition of **Z** was given as C = 52.2%, H = 13.0%, O = 34.8%.

(a) Calculate the empirical formula of **Z**.

(b) Suggest a structure for compound **Z**.

(c) The infra-red spectrum of **Z** is shown below.

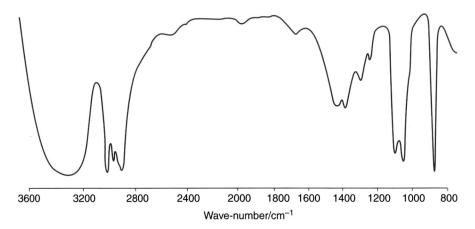

Wave-number/cm^{-1}

How does this support the structure you have given to **Z**?

Index

Use of *italics* indicates an illustration.

INDEX